# The
# Anatomy
# Colouring
# Book

# The Anatomy Colouring Book

Illustrations by **James Berrangé**

Text by
**Dr C R Constant** MA, MB, BCh, BAO, MCh, LLM, FRCS
**Dr Cecilia Brassett** MB BChir, MChir, FRCS
**Michelle Spear** BSc (Hons), MSc FIBMS

NEW
HOLLAND

First published in the UK in 2011 by New Holland Publishers (UK) Ltd
London · Cape Town · Sydney · Auckland

Garfield House, 86–88 Edgware Road, London W2 2EA, United Kingdom
www.newhollandpublishers.com

80 McKenzie Street, Cape Town 8001, South Africa
Unit 1, 66 Gibbes Street, Chatswood, NSW 2067, Australia
218 Lake Road, Northcote, Auckland, New Zealand

ISBN 978 1 84773 869 1

Publisher: Guy Hobbs
Production: Marion Storz
Design: Phil Kay
Scanning: Photoplate Digital Prepress, Cape Town

10 9 8 7 6 5 4 3 2 1

Cover repro: Pica Digital Pte Ltd, Singapore
Printed & bound by Replika Press Pvt Ltd, India

# CONTENTS

# INTRODUCTION

This collection of anatomical drawings is designed to both teach and stimulate interest in anatomy. By colouring in the illustrations, the reader is encouraged to closely examine the material and the text, thereby learning more about the anatomical relationships of the structures and the names of the areas being coloured in. The reader is made aware not only of the two-dimensional page but also the three-dimensional aspect, which is so important in understanding and learning anatomy.

The book is designed for those who are studying anatomy, as a tool to enhance understanding and assist revision of the topic. However, it will be equally valuable for those with little or no anatomical knowledge, as it provides a very worthwhile introduction to the anatomy of the human body. The book is not meant to replace anatomy textbooks or atlases, but it should act as an enjoyable and worthwhile interlude during the study of anatomy. Part of its value lies in the fact that the reader can put it down at any time and return to it when convenient or when the moods suits. The reader can vary the intensity with which he or she approaches it, depending on the extent to which the reading or the colouring matches his or her interest.

While it is entirely up to the reader to choose the colours used in this book, there is, generally speaking, a recognised convention for colour usage for specific structures:

- Arteries containing oxygenated blood are conventionally coloured red
- Veins containing deoxygenated blood are traditionally coloured blue
- Nerves are generally coloured yellow (the authors suggest a bright yellow for nerves and a very faint yellow for fascia)
- Muscles in real life are reddish brown and colouring them using light brown is reasonable
- Ligaments, being more solid structures, are often pale in real life, and are probably best coloured in grey, with bones outlined in black
- Different shades from grey to black can be used to fill in the bones, where appropriate
- Cartilage covering joint surfaces or in areas such as the knee, ear and nose are often depicted as yellow, using a slightly lighter shade of yellow than that used for the nerves
- For large hollow structures, such as the bowel, it is best to use a neutral colour, as the outer surface of the bowel is often a pale colour with markings similar to arterial supply and venous drainage
- The liver is a brown or mauve colour in real life, which is usually reflected in drawings
- The components of the biliary system, including the common bile duct, hepatic ducts, cystic duct and gallbladder are traditionally coloured in dark green, similar to the colour of bile
- The kidneys, being a solid organ, can be a dark colour, such as mauve or brown; the readers can use their imagination in combining colours to give different hues to

different organs, allowing them to be easily distinguished

- The pancreas and other endocrine organs are variable, in both atlases and in real life. The pancreas is a pale cream or yellow colour, while the thyroid gland is dark. The adrenal glands overlying each kidney should be coloured slightly differently from the kidneys, in order to distinguish them, while the spleen, sitting in the upper left-hand quadrant of the abdomen and covered by ribs, is dark, similar to the kidneys and liver, but somewhat lighter
- The mucous membranes of the mouth and other orifices are generally coloured pink
- The solid and hollow organs within the pelvis (uterus, bladder and rectum) should be appropriately coloured to be similar to their structure

No matter which colours you choose (there is no correct or incorrect colour coding), the fully coloured book will provide a useful reference to anyone interested in anatomy.

We hope you enjoy your colouring!

Dr C R Constant, Dr Cecilia Brassett and Michelle Spear

# ABOUT THE AUTHORS

**Dr C R Constant**

| | |
|---|---|
| Degrees: | MA, MB, BCh, BAO, MCh, LLM, FRCS |
| Positions: | University clinical anatomist |
| | Department of Physiology, Development and Neuroscience |
| | University of Cambridge, UK |
| And | Emeritus consultant orthopaedic and trauma surgeon |
| | Visiting shoulder and elbow specialist |
| | Addenbrooke's Hospital, Cambridge, UK |
| And | Senior member and college lecturer in medical sciences |
| | Robinson College, Cambridge, UK |

**Dr Cecilia Brassett**

| | |
|---|---|
| Degrees: | MB BChir, MChir, FRCS |
| Positions: | University clinical anatomist |
| | Department of Physiology, Development and Neuroscience |
| | University of Cambridge, UK |
| And | Fellow and college lecturer in medical sciences |
| | Magdalene College, Cambridge, UK |

**Ms Michelle Spear**

| | |
|---|---|
| Degrees: | BSc (Hons), MSc FIBMS |
| Positions: | Deputy clinical anatomist |
| | Department of Physiology, Development and Neuroscience |
| | University of Cambridge, UK |
| And | Fellow and college lecturer in anatomy |
| | Murray Edwards College, Cambridge, UK |

# THE NERVOUS SYSTEM

## ORGANISATION OF THE AUTONOMIC NERVOUS SYSTEM

The autonomic nervous system is concerned with the non-voluntary control of visceral structures such as glands, blood vessels and the gut. The system is widely distributed throughout the body and consists of neurons arranged as ganglia and strands of fibres that interlace to produce plexuses. The main aggregations of autonomic elements are found in the thorax and abdomen close to the viscera that they supply, but all parts of the body are supplied. As a generalisation, the sympathetic nervous system prepares the body for response to the external environment or crisis – so-called 'fight or flight'; the parasympathetic nervous system is concerned with conservation and building up of energy – 'rest and digest'. The parasympathetics have a craniosacral outflow – that is, preganglionic parasympathetic fibres are carried by either the cranial or the pelvic nerves. The sympathetic outflow is described as thoracolumbar because preganglionic fibres arise in the T1–L2 region of the spinal cord.

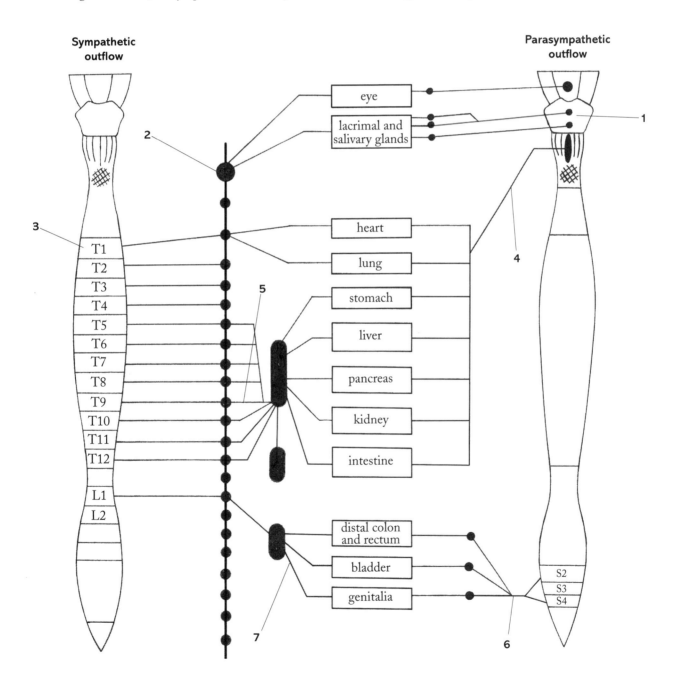

**Key: 1.** cranial parasympathetics  **2.** cervical sympathetic chain  **3.** sympathetic outflow (T1–L2)
**4.** vagus nerve  **5.** thoracic splanchnic nerves  **6.** pelvic splanchnic  **7.** hypogastric nerves

## SPINAL CORD AND SPINAL NERVES

There are 31 pairs of spinal nerves. These are grouped as cervical, thoracic, lumbar, sacral and coccygeal, in relation to the vertebrae between which they emerge. Each nerve communicates with the spinal cord and is formed by a dorsal root, which conveys sensory information, and a motor root, which conveys motor instructions, making the spinal nerve a mixed nerve. The grey matter of the spinal cord contains the cell bodies of sensory and motor neurons, and the white matter contains myelinated axons. T1–L2 spinal nerves also convey preganglionic sympathetic fibres.

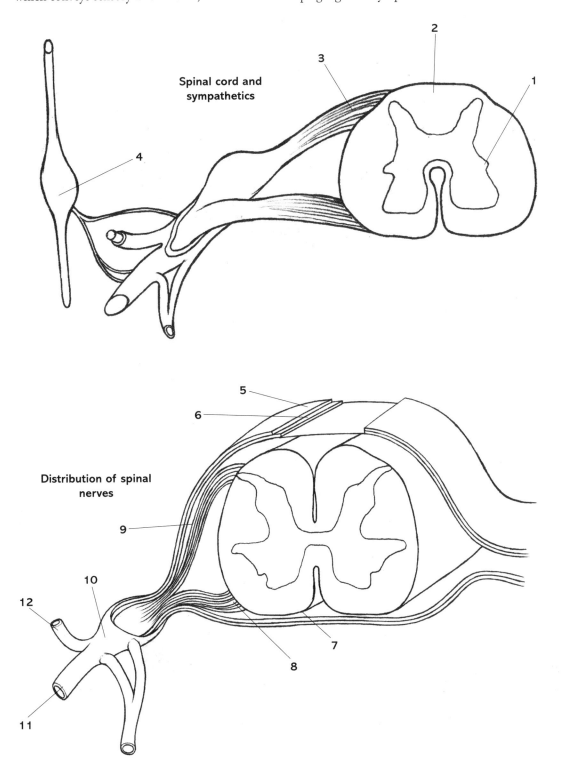

Spinal cord and sympathetics

Distribution of spinal nerves

**Key: 1.** lateral horn grey matter (T1–L2 region only)  **2.** spinal cord  **3.** preganglionic fibres  **4.** sympathetic ganglion
**5.** dura mater (cutaway)  **6.** arachnoid mater  **7.** spinal cord  **8.** ventral root  **9.** dorsal root  **10.** spinal nerve
**11.** anterior ramus of spinal nerve  **12.** posterior ramus of spinal nerve

# UPPER LIMB NERVES: THE BRACHIAL PLEXUS CONCEPTUAL OVERVIEW

The anterior rami of spinal nerves combine to form plexi – cervical, brachial, lumbar and sacral. Their arrangement and distribution is complex.

The brachial plexus is formed by the anterior rami of the fifth, sixth, seventh and eighth cervical spinal nerves and the first thoracic nerve. Nerve roots that contribute to the plexus are located in the posterior triangle of the neck, between the anterior and middle scalene muscles; the trunks also cross the posterior triangle of the neck. The divisions pass beneath the clavicle, and the cords pass into the axilla, where they are named in relation to the axillary artery.

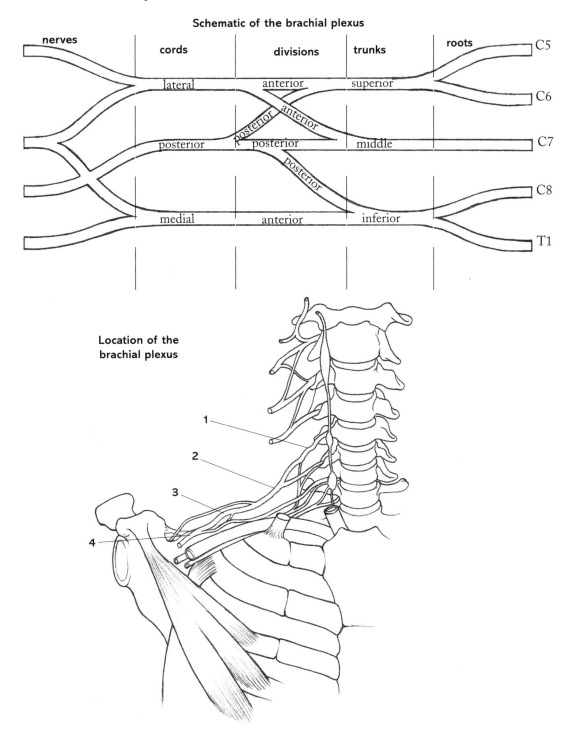

**Schematic of the brachial plexus**

**Location of the brachial plexus**

**Key: 1.** anterior rami of C5–T1 **2.** trunks (superior, middle, inferior) **3.** divisions (anterior, posterior) **4.** cords (anterior, posterior)

## BRACHIAL PLEXUS AND NERVES

The brachial plexus ensures that each of the upper limb muscles are supplied by multiple spinal levels. The radial nerve (C5–T1) supplies the skin and muscles of the posterior (extensor) compartment of the arm and forearm. The median nerve (C6–T1) supplies muscles of the forearm and hand, as does the ulnar nerve (C8–T1). The musculocutaneous nerve (C5, 6, 7) supplies muscles of the arm and skin of the forearm. The axillary nerve (C5, 6) supplies the deltoid muscle, its overlying skin and the teres minor muscle.

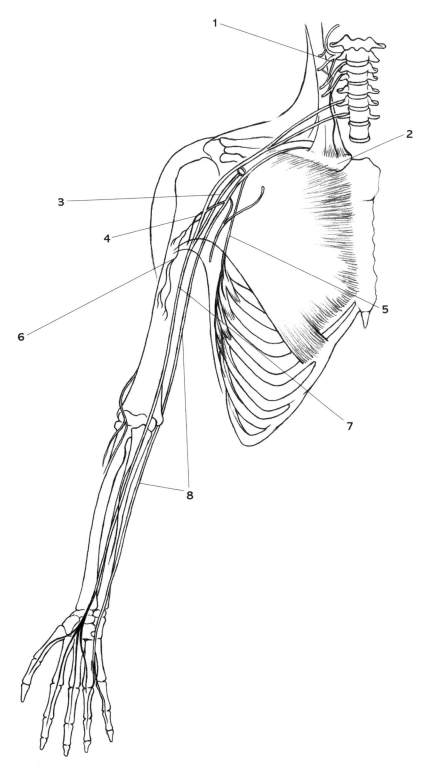

**Key: 1.** nerve roots  **2.** clavicle  **3.** radial nerve  **4.** axillary (*circumflex*) nerve  **5.** long thoracic nerve
**6.** musculocutaneous nerve (muscular branches)  **7.** median nerve  **8.** ulnar nerve

## LOWER LIMB

The femoral nerve (L2–L4) passes through the psoas muscle, and then beneath the inguinal ligament, lateral to the femoral artery, where after only a short course on the anterior thigh (about 5cm/2in), it breaks up into its terminal branches.

These branches supply the muscles and skin of the anterior thigh and give the saphenous nerve, which supplies sensation to the medial aspect of the leg, foot, ankle and the big toe.

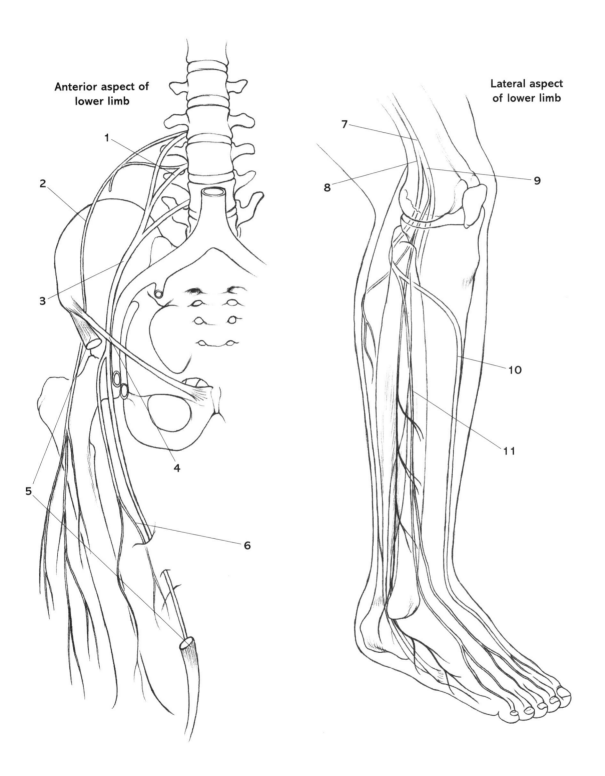

**Anterior aspect of lower limb**

**Lateral aspect of lower limb**

**Key: 1.** roots L2–L4  **2.** lateral cutaneous nerve of thigh  **3.** femoral nerve  **4.** inguinal ligament  **5.** cut edge of sartorius muscle  **6.** medial cutaneous nerve of thigh

**7.** sciatic nerve  **8.** common fibular nerve  **9.** tibial nerve  **10.** deep fibular nerve  **11.** superficial fibular nerve

# MEDIAL AND POSTERIOR ASPECT OF THE LOWER LIMB

The sciatic nerve (L4–L5 S1–3) is the largest nerve in the human body. The nerve emerges from the greater sciatic foramen in the pelvis, distal to the piriformis, and lies under the cover of the gluteus maximus, where it may be at risk in a misplaced intramuscular injection. The nerve then crosses the posterior surface of the ischium and descends on the adductor magnus.

The sciatic nerve terminates by dividing into the tibial and common fibular (peroneal) nerves. The level of this division varies but usually occurs at the mid-thigh. The trunk of the sciatic nerve supplies the hamstring muscles (biceps, semimembranosus, semitendinosus) as well as the adductor magnus. All muscular branches, except the one to the short head of the biceps, arise on the medial side of the nerve.

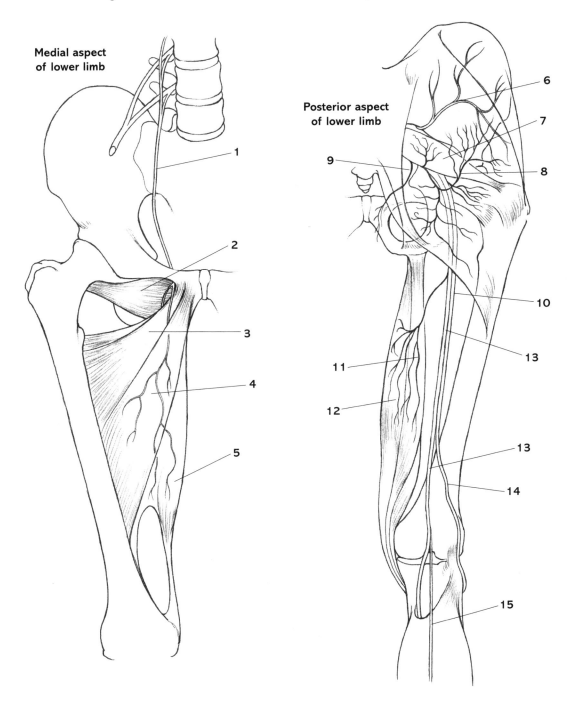

**Medial aspect of lower limb**

**Posterior aspect of lower limb**

**Key: 1.** obturator nerve **2.** obturator externus muscle **3.** adductor brevis muscle **4.** adductor longus muscle **5.** adductor magnus muscle

**6.** superior gluteal nerve **7.** piriformis **8.** inferior gluteal nerve **9.** posterior cutaneous nerve of thigh **10.** sciatic nerve **11.** nerve to semimembranosus **12.** nerve to semitendinosus **13.** tibial nerve **14.** common fibular nerve **15.** sural nerve

## HEAD AND NECK: CRANIAL NERVES

Twelve pairs of cranial nerves originate in the brain and pass through certain foramina of the skull to be distributed in and around the head and neck. The exception is the vagus nerve, which continues into the thorax and abdomen. The cranial nerves are named and numbered sequentially with Roman numerals, progressing rostrally to caudally.

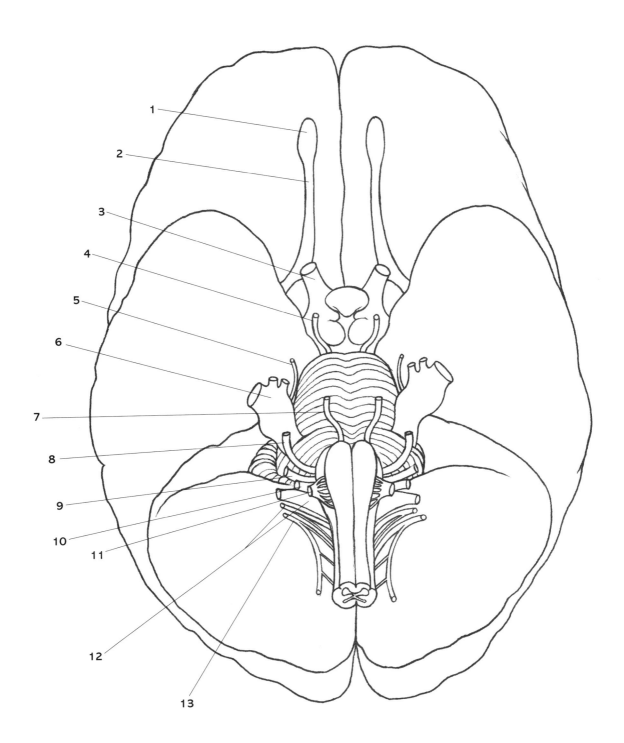

**Key: 1.** olfactory bulb  **2.** olfactory tract  **3.** optic nerve  **4.** oculomotor nerve  **5.** trochlear nerve  **6.** trigeminal nerve
**7.** abducent nerve  **8.** facial nerve  **9.** vestibulocochlear nerve  **10.** glossopharyngeal nerve  **11.** hypoglossal nerve
**12.** vagus nerve  **13.** accessory nerve

## HEAD AND NECK: TRIGEMINAL NERVE

The trigeminal nerve carries both sensory and
motor nerve fibres. As a sensory nerve, it
conveys information about the face and scalp.
Postganglionic autonomic nerve fibres
are also carried by its branches, as they are
widely distributed.

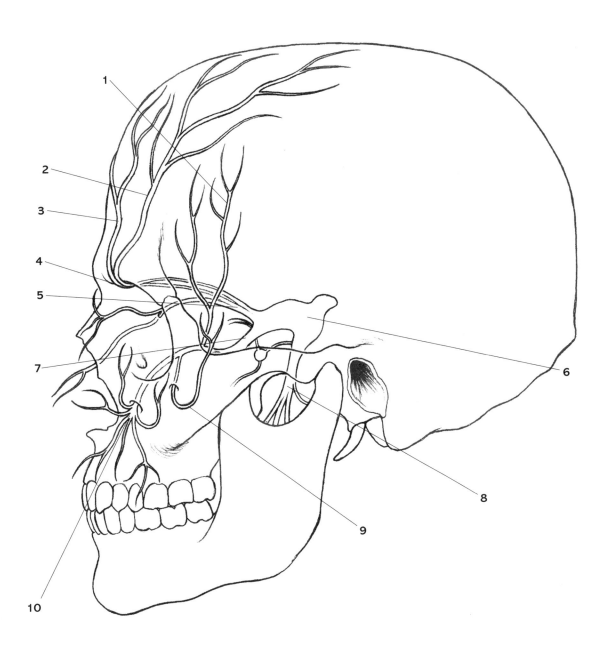

**Key: 1.** zygomaticotemporal branch  **2.** supraorbital nerve  **3.** frontal nerve  **4.** lacrimal nerve
**5.** ophthalmic nerve  **6** trigeminal nerve  **7.** maxillary nerve  **8.** mandibular nerve  **9.** zygomaticofacial branch
**10.** infraorbital (infratrochlear) nerve

# HEAD AND NECK: MANDIBULAR NERVE

The trigeminal nerve has three branches:
ophthalmic, maxillary and mandibular.
The first two branches are purely sensory; the
mandibular nerve also carries motor fibres
to the muscles of mastication.

**Branches of the man-
dibular nerve**

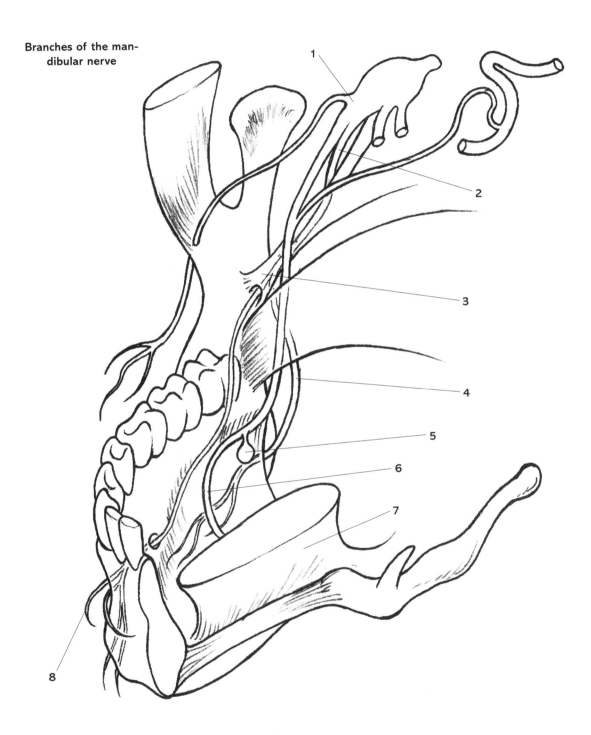

**Key: 1.** mandibular nerve  **2.** inferior alveolar nerve  **3.** inferior alveolar nerve entering mandibular canal  **4.** nerve
to mylohyoid muscle  **5.** submandibular ganglion  **6.** lingual nerve  **7.** genioglossus muscle  **8.** mental nerve

## CONNECTIONS OF THE FACIAL NERVE IN THE TEMPORAL BONE

The facial nerve is the source of motor innervation to all muscles of facial expression. It also carries preganglionic parasympathetic axons from the brain destined for the lacrimal, submandibular, sublingual and nasal mucous glands, as well as axons for taste from the anterior two thirds of the tongue to the brain. The facial nerve is responsible for general sensation of the skin lining the external auditory meatus. Only motor axons emerge from the stylomastoid foramen. The facial nerve therefore gives off several branches whilst in the temporal bone, these are shown below.

**The facial nerve**

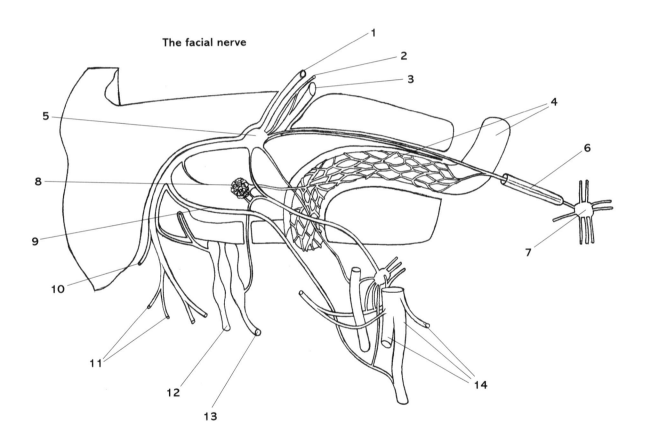

**Key: 1.** motor root of facial nerve  **2.** sensory root of facial nerve  **3.** vestibulocochlear nerve (auditory nerve)
**4.** internal carotid artery with sympathetic plexus  **5.** ganglion of facial nerve  **6.** nerve of pterygoid canal
**7.** pterygopalatine ganglion  **8.** tympanic plexus  **9.** chorda tympani  **10.** posterior auricular nerve  **11.** nerves to stylohyoid and posterior belly  **12.** vagus nerve  **13.** glossopharyngeal nerve  **14.** branches of the trigeminal nerve

## DISTRIBUTION OF TRIGEMINAL AND
## FACIAL NERVES ON THE FACE

Note: Features 1–3 and 6 are derived from the trigeminal nerve, features, 4, 5, 7, 8 and 9 are branches of the facial nerve.

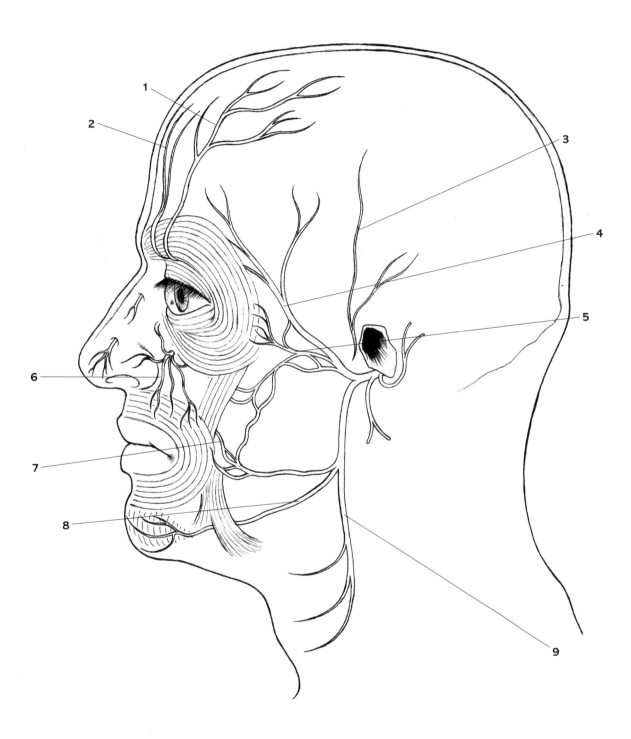

**Key: 1.** supraorbital nerve **2.** supratrochlear nerve. **3.** auriculo-temporal nerve **4.** temporal branch of CN VII
**5.** zygomatic branch of CN VII **6.** infraorbital nerve **7.** buccal nerve **8.** mandibular nerve **9.** cervical nerve

DISTRIBUTION OF TRIGEMINAL AND
FACIAL NERVES IN THE FACE

# THORAX

The vagus nerve, cranial nerve X, is the most widely distributed cranial nerve, containing a large number of parasympathetic fibres. It supplies afferent (sensory) fibres to the pharynx, oesophagus, stomach, larynx, trachea and lungs, and efferent fibres to the smooth muscle of these viscera, in addition to supplying the heart and abdominal viscera.

**The vagus nerve**

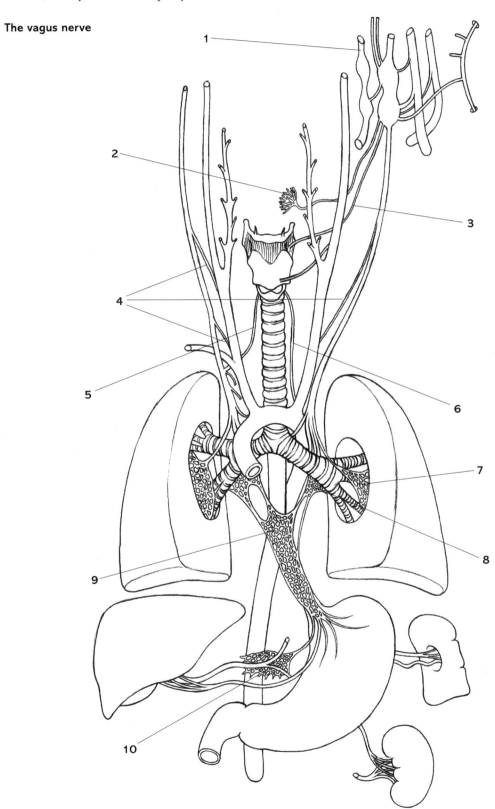

**Key: 1.** left vagus nerve  **2.** pharyngeal plexus  **3.** left superior laryngeal nerve  **4.** cardiac branches to cardiac plexus  **5.** right recurrent laryngeal nerve  **6.** left recurrent laryngeal nerve  **7.** posterior pulmonary plexus  **8.** anterior pulmonary plexus  **9.** oesophagus carrying right and left vagal trunks  **10.** celiac plexus

## A TYPICAL THORACIC NERVE

The anterior rami of the thoracic spinal nerves,
with the exception of T1, do not form a plexus
but instead remain as 12 separate nerves. The
first 11 nerves become the intercostal nerves;
the twelfth nerve becomes subcostal.

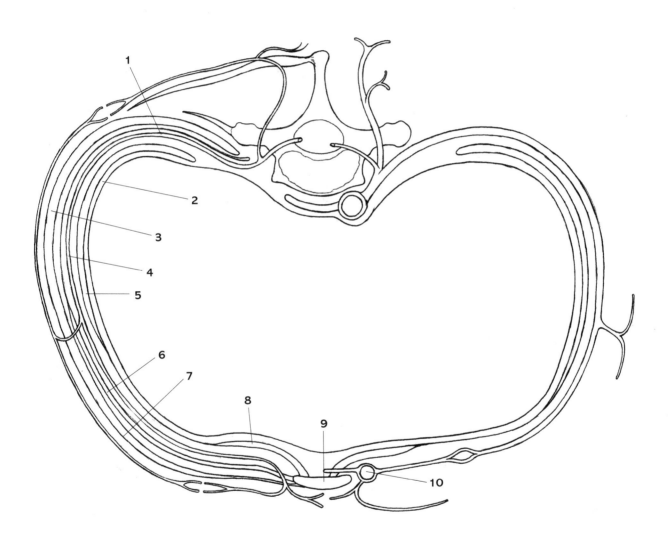

**Key: 1.** anterior root of spinal nerve  **2.** pleura  **3.** external intercostal muscle  **4.** intercostal nerve  **5.** innermost intercostal muscle (sterno-costalis)  **6.** internal intercostal muscle  **7.** intercostal membrane  **8.** sternum  **9.** internal thoracic (mammary) vessels  **10.** ganglion of sympathetic trunk

## THE ABDOMEN AND PELVIS: THE LUMBAR PLEXUS

The lumbar plexus originates from the anterior rami of L1–L4. The trunks of the plexus traverse the psoas major muscle and emerge from its lateral border. There are two exceptions: the obturator nerve appears at the medial aspect of the tendon, and the genitofemoral nerve appears on the anterior aspect of the muscle.

The principal branches of the plexus are the femoral and obturator nerves.

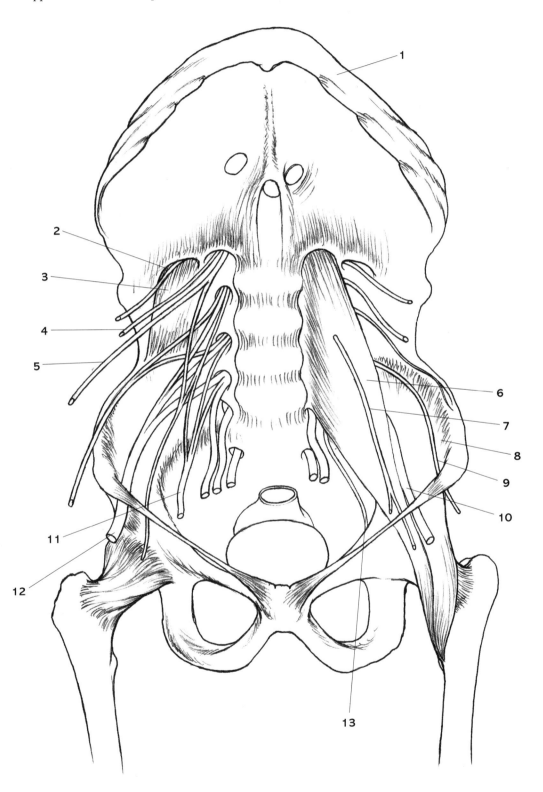

**Key: 1.** diaphragm **2.** subcostal nerve **3.** quadratus lumborum muscle **4.** iliohypogastric nerve **5.** ilioinguinal nerve **6.** psoas major muscle **7.** genitofemoral nerve **8.** Iliacus muscle **9.** lateral cutaneous nerve of thigh **10.** lumbosacral trunk **11.** obturator nerve **12.** femoral nerve **13.** obturator nerve

## AUTONOMICS OF THE ABDOMEN AND PELVIS

Structures of the abdomen, up to two thirds of the transverse colon, receive parasympathetic nerve fibres via the vagus nerve. From the splenic flexure of the colon onwards, parasympathetics are supplied by the pelvic splanchnic nerves. Sympathetic nerve fibres descend from the abdomen as the thoracic splanchnic nerves – greater, lesser and least.

The greater splanchnic nerve (T5–T9) contributes to the celiac plexus, the lesser splanchnic nerve (T10, T11) contributes to the superior mesenteric plexus, and the least splanchnic nerve supplies the inferior mesenteric plexus. The inferior mesenteric plexus also receives sympathetics from the hypogastric plexus.

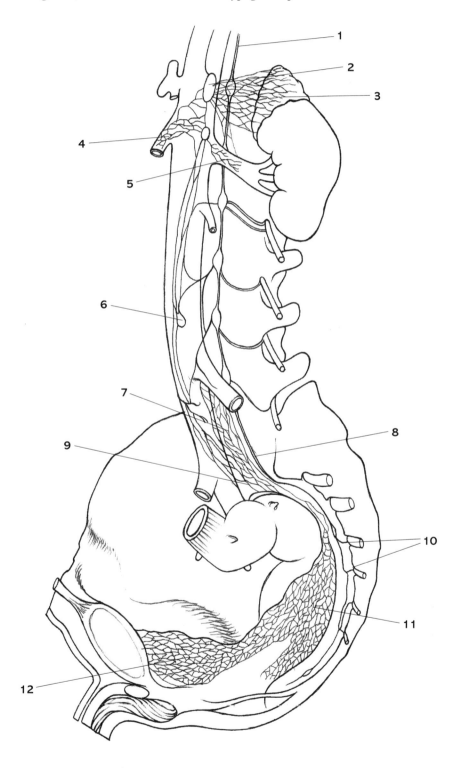

**Key: 1.** sympathetic chain  **2.** celiac ganglion  **3.** suprarenal plexus  **4.** superior mesenteric plexus  **5.** renal plexus
**6.** inferior mesenteric plexus  **7.** hypogastric plexus  **8.** sympathetic trunk  **9.** pelvic plexus  **10.** pelvic sphanchnic
nerves **11.** rectal plexus **12.** vesical plexus

## THE SACRAL PLEXUS: THE PUDENDAL NERVE

The pudendal nerve (S2–S4) provides the principal innervation of the perineum. It has a complex course, passing from the pelvis, briefly through the gluteal region, along the side wall of the ischiorectal fossa, and through the deep perineal pouch, to end by supplying the skin of the external genitalia.

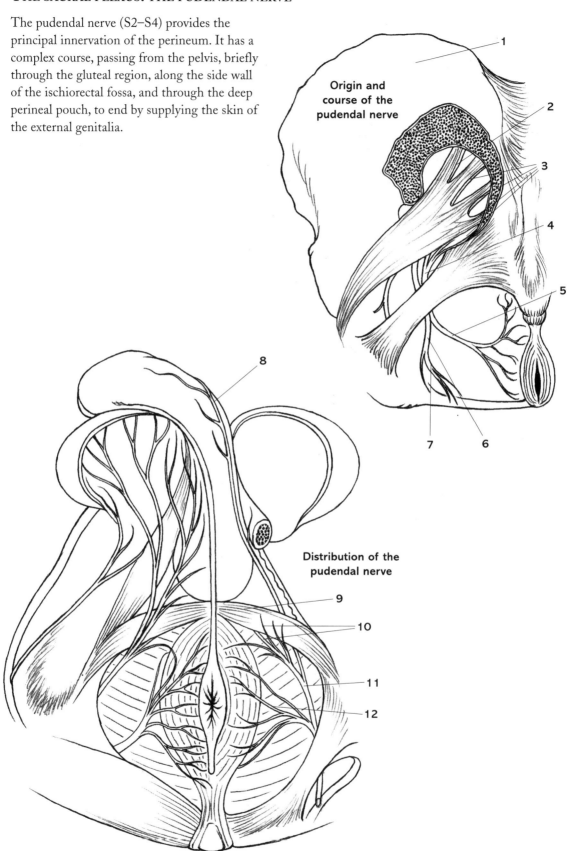

Origin and course of the pudendal nerve

Distribution of the pudendal nerve

**Key: 1.** ilium **2.** lumbosacral trunk **3.** anterior rami of S1–4 **4.** pudendal nerve **5.** inferior rectal nerve
**6.** pudendal nerve **7.** perineal nerve

**8.** dorsal nerve of penis **9.** transverse perineal muscle **10.** superficial and deep perineal nerves **11.** pudendal nerve **12.** inferior rectal nerve

# THE ENDOCRINE SYSTEM

The endocrine system consists of endocrine glands that produce hormones and organs that have other functions but also contain hormone-producing cells. The former group comprises the pituitary, pineal, thyroid, parathyroid and adrenal glands, while the latter group includes the thymus gland, liver, stomach, pancreas, kidneys and gonads.

The hypothalamus is the primary regulating organ of the endocrine glands. It projects two types of efferent fibres: descending neural efferents into the brain stem, which influence the endocrine glands via the autonomic nervous system, and hormonal efferents, which regulate the secondary endocrine glands through neurohormones.

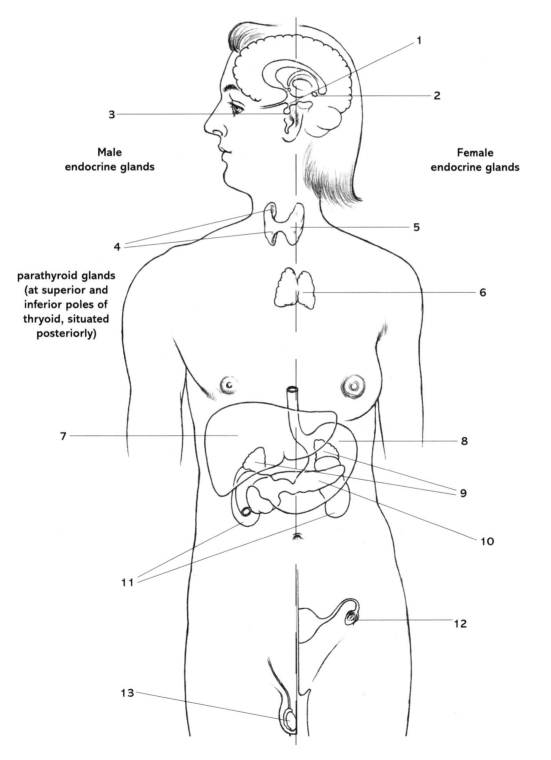

Male
endocrine glands

Female
endocrine glands

parathyroid glands
(at superior and
inferior poles of
thryoid, situated
posteriorly)

**Key: 1.** hypothalamus **2.** pineal gland **3.** pituitary gland **4.** parathyroid glands **5.** thyroid gland **6.** thymus gland **7.** liver **8.** stomach **9.** adrenal glands **10.** pancreas **11.** kidneys **12.** ovary **13.** testis

## THE PITUITARY GLAND

The pituitary gland occupies the sella turcica (pituitary fossa) of the sphenoid bone and produces hormones that influence the activities of other endocrine glands. The roof of the fossa is dura mater (diaphragma sellae), which is pierced by the pituitary stalk (infundibulum).

The gland is related to the optic chiasma superiorly, the cavernous sinus and internal carotid artery bilaterally, and the sphenoidal sinus antero-inferiorly. It has an anterior lobe (adenohypophysis) and a posterior lobe (neurohypophysis). Hypothalamic hormones are secreted to the anterior lobe via the hypothalamic-hypophyseal portal system.

The pineal gland is about 10mm (just under half an inch) long and lies in the roof of the third ventricle of the brain. It produces the hormone melatonin.

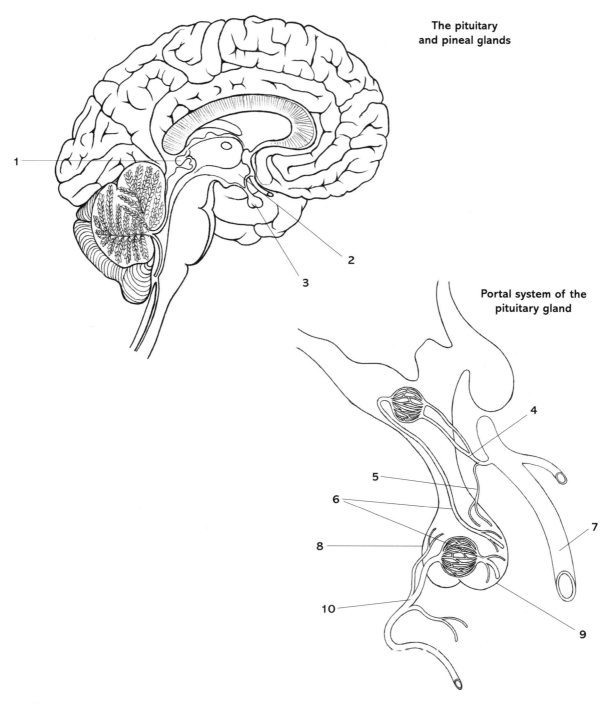

**The pituitary and pineal glands**

**Portal system of the pituitary gland**

**Key: 1.** pineal gland **2.** hypothalamus **3.** pituitary gland

**4.** superior hypophyseal artery **5.** middle hypophyseal artery **6.** portal vessels **7.** internal carotid artery
**8.** posterior lobe **9.** anterior lobe **10.** inferior hypophyseal artery

# THE THYROID GLAND

The thyroid gland lies in the anterior triangle of the neck. It consists of two lateral lobes united by an isthmus lying over the second to fourth tracheal rings. It produces thyroxine and calcitonin.

It is supplied by the superior thyroid (branch of the external carotid) and inferior thyroid (branch of the thyrocervical trunk of subclavian) arteries. These arteries are related to the external branch of the superior laryngeal and recurrent laryngeal nerves respectively. Venous drainage is via superior, middle (to internal jugular), and inferior thyroid (to left brachiocephalic) veins.

The four parathyroid glands lie posterior to the lateral lobes of the thyroid. Their position is variable, especially the inferior ones. They secrete parathormone.

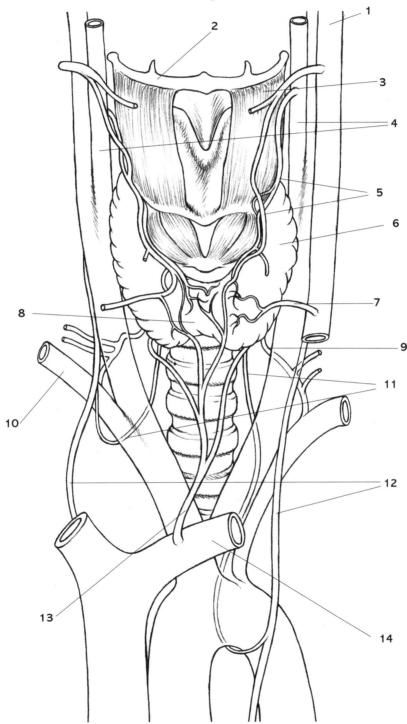

**Key: 1.** internal jugular vein **2.** hyoid bone **3.** thyrohyoid (muscle) **4.** external carotid artery **5.** superior thyroid artery and vein **6.** thyroid gland **7.** middle thyroid vein **8.** isthmus **9.** inferior thyroid artery **10.** subclavian artery **11.** left and right recurrent laryngeal nerves **12.** left and right vagus nerves **13.** inferior thyroid veins **14.** left brachiocephalic vein

## THE ADRENAL GLANDS

The adrenal glands lie outside the renal capsules and are asymmetrical. The right adrenal is pyramidal and embraces the upper pole of the right kidney; the left adrenal is crescentic and embraces the medial border of the left kidney above the hilum. They are related posteriorly to the diaphragm, with the right adrenal being related to the bare area of the liver and the inferior vena cava. Each gland consists of the cortex and the medulla and is supplied by three arteries (branches of the inferior phrenic, aorta and renal arteries). On the right, the adrenal vein drains into the inferior vena cava and, on the left, into the left renal vein. The cortex produces cortisol, aldosterone and androgens, while the medulla secretes adrenaline (epinephrine) and noradrenaline (norepinephrine).

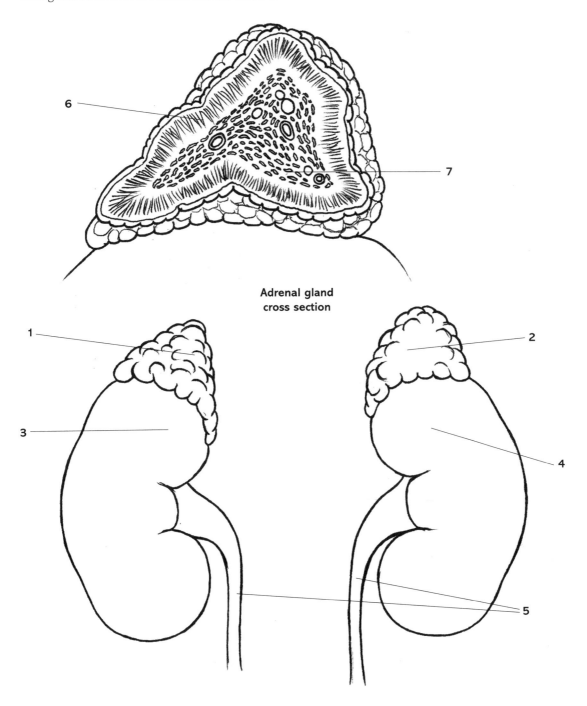

**Adrenal gland cross section**

**Key: 1.** right adrenal gland  **2.** left adrenal gland  **3.** right kidney  **4.** left kidney  **5.** ureters
**6.** adrenal cortex  **7.** adrenal medulla

# THE CARDIOVASCULAR SYSTEM

## ORGANISATION OF THE CARDIOVASCULAR SYSTEM: BLOOD VESSEL STRUCTURE

Blood vessels have three layers. The inner tunica intima consists of endothelium, a basement membrane and internal elastic lamina. The tunica media consists of circular smooth muscle and elastin fibres. The outer tunica adventitia is connective tissue.

The thickness and composition of the layers vary with blood vessel type and diameter. Large elastic arteries (e.g. aorta and pulmonary trunk) are thin-walled with large diameters. The tunica media has many elastin fibres but little smooth muscle.

Muscular (distributing) arteries (femoral, brachial) are thick-walled with small diameters. The tunica media has abundant smooth muscle and some elastin. Arterioles are the smallest arteries. The tunica media consists of smooth muscle cells and a few elastin fibres. Venules are endothelium surrounded by a few smooth muscle cells. Small veins are venules surrounded by a layer of smooth muscle. Large veins (venae cavae) contain less smooth muscle and elastin than arteries of the same size.

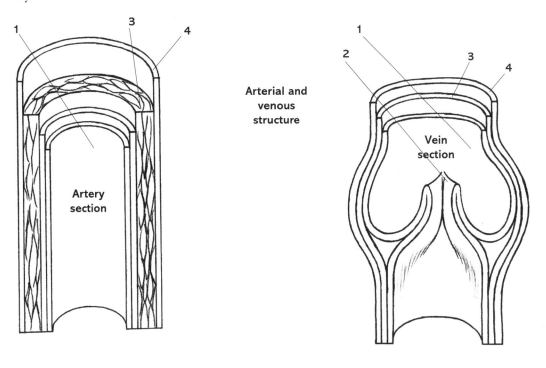

Arterial and venous structure

Artery section

Vein section

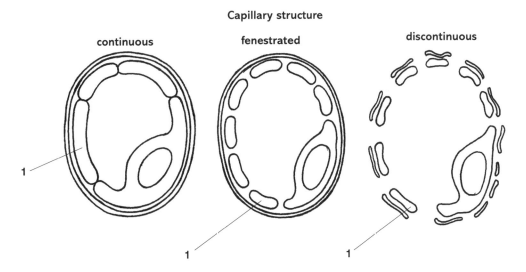

Capillary structure

continuous    fenestrated    discontinuous

**Key: 1.** endothelium **2.** valve **3.** tunica media **4.** tunica adventitia

## UPPER LIMB ARTERIAL SUPPLY

The arterial supply to the upper limb passes through the root of the neck as the subclavian artery, crosses the axilla as the axillary artery, and is continued along the arm as the brachial artery, giving off a deep branch, called the profunda brachii. In the forearm the brachial artery bifurcates at the level of the radial head to become radial and ulnar arteries. The radial and ulnar arteries anastomose to form the palmar arches, the radial artery being the major contributor to the deep palmar arch and the ulnar to the superficial arch.

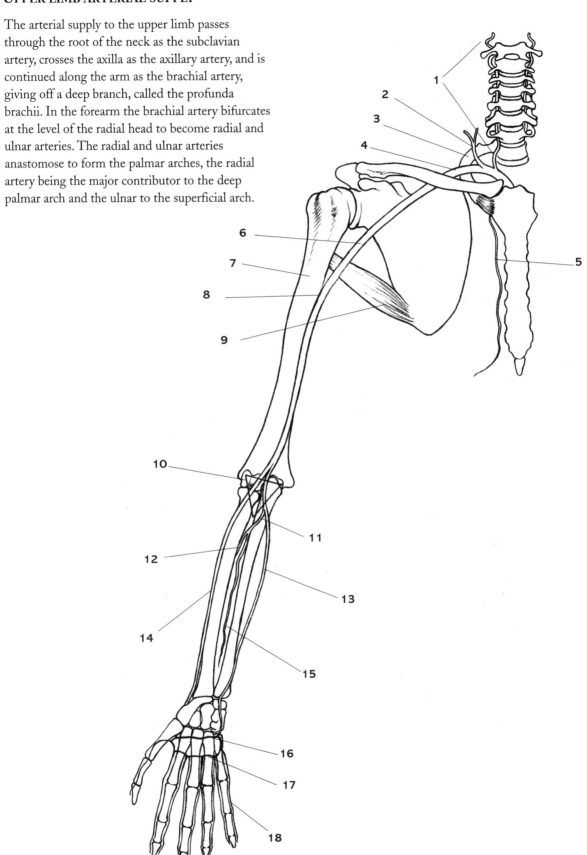

**Key: 1.** vertebral artery **2.** thyrocervical trunk **3.** first rib **4.** subclavian artery **5.** internal thoracic artery **6.** axillary artery **7.** humerus **8.** brachial artery **9.** teres major muscle **10.** cubital fossa **11.** common interosseous artery **12.** posterior interosseous artery **13.** ulnar artery **14.** radial artery **15.** anterior interosseous artery **16.** deep palmar arch **17.** superficial palmar arch **18.** digital artery

## UPPER LIMB VENOUS DRAINAGE

Deep veins follow arteries. The cephalic and basilic veins drain the skin and superficial structures of the upper limb. The cephalic vein commences on the lateral side of the dorsal venous arch and the basilic vein commences on the medial side; each drains to the axillary vein.

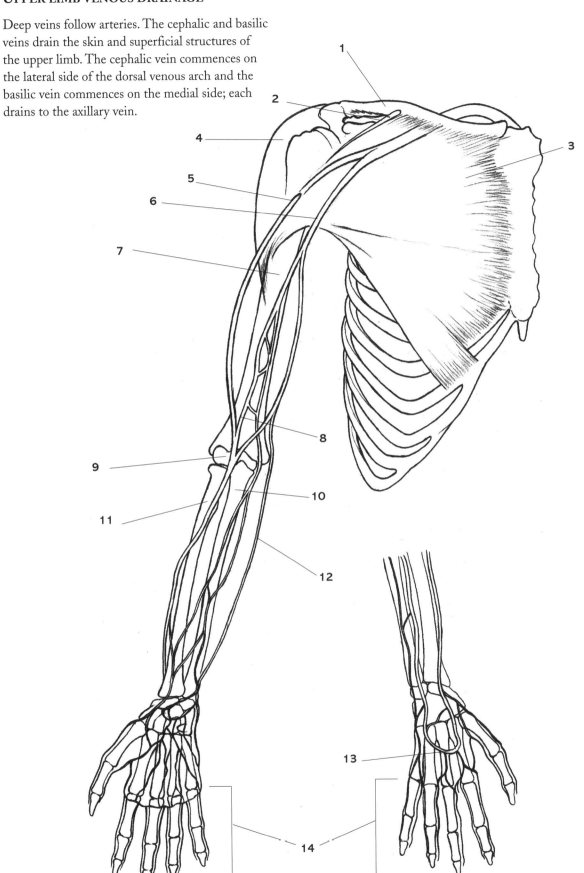

**Key: 1.** clavicle  **2.** deltopectoral groove  **3.** pectoralis major  **4.** deltoid **5.** cephalic vein  **6.** axillary vein
**7.** humerus  **8.** median cubital vein  **9.** cubital fossa  **10.** ulna  **11.** radius  **12.** basilic vein  **13.** dorsal venous
arch  **14.** digital veins

## LOWER LIMB ARTERIAL SUPPLY

The external iliac artery extends to the inguinal ligament, at which point it becomes the femoral artery. The femoral artery passes through the proximal two thirds of the thigh and terminates at the adductor hiatus, becoming the popliteal artery. The anterior and posterior tibial arteries are the terminal branches of the popliteal artery.

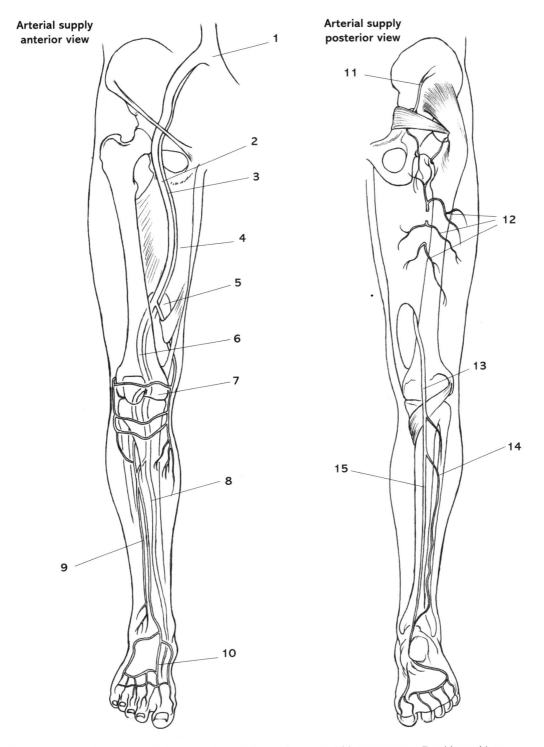

**Arterial supply anterior view**

**Arterial supply posterior view**

**Key: 1.** common iliac artery  **2.** femoral artery  **3.** femoral vein  **4.** adductor magnus  **5.** adductor hiatus
**6.** popliteal artery  **7.** genicular arteries  **8.** posterior tibial artery  **9.** anterior tibial artery  **10.** dorsalis pedis artery

**11.** superior gluteal artery  **12.** profunda femoris (deep branches of femoral artery)  **13.** popliteal artery
**14.** fibular artery  **15.** posterior tibial artery

## LOWER LIMB VENOUS DRAINAGE

Deep veins of the lower limb are named after the arteries that they follow and are not shown.

The superficial veins of the lower limb terminate in two trunks, one of which, the short saphenous vein, passes from the lateral aspect of the dorsal venous arch to the popliteal vein. The other trunk, the long saphenous vein, extends from the medial aspect of the dorsal venous arch to the femoral vein. These veins can become varicosed.

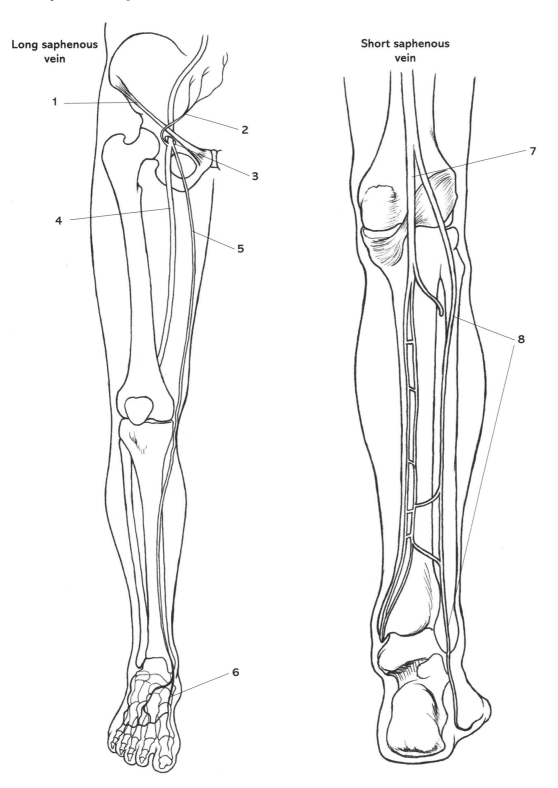

**Key: 1.** inguinal  ligament **2.** superficial epigastric vein  **3.** saphenous opening  **4.** femoral vein  **5.** long saphenous vein  **6.** dorsal venous arch

**7.** popliteal vein  **8.** short saphenous vein

# HEAD AND NECK: ARTERIES AND VEINS

The vessels distributed to the head and neck are derived principally from the carotids. The common carotid artery bifurcates to give internal and external branches. The internal carotid artery does not branch until it reaches the brain; all vessels to the neck and face are derived from the external carotid artery. Veins of the head and neck lack valves, therefore a strict drainage pattern does not exist. In their course, veins follow arteries.

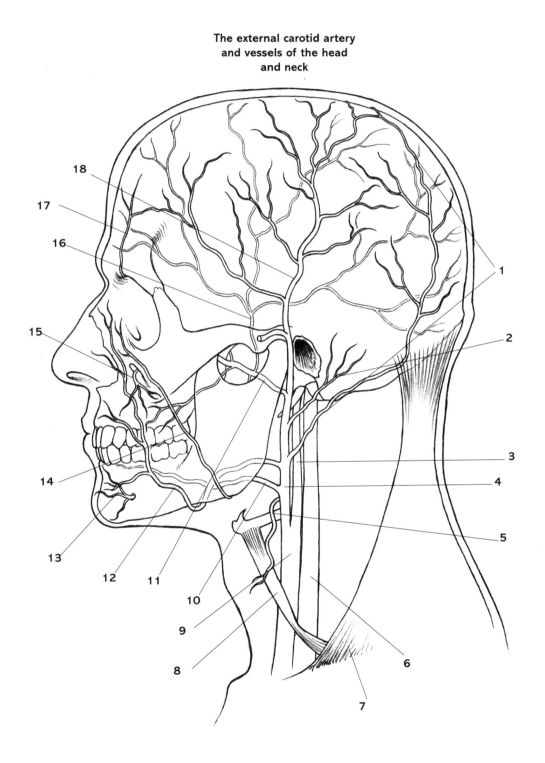

**The external carotid artery and vessels of the head and neck**

**Key: 1.** occipital artery  **2.** posterior auricular artery  **3.** internal carotid artery  **4.** external carotid artery  **5.** superior thyroid artery  **6.** internal jugular vein  **7.** trapezius muscle  **8.** omohyoid muscle  **9.** common carotid artery
**10.** lingual artery  **11.** maxillary artery  **12.** facial artery  **13.** mental artery  **14.** common facial vein
**15.** infraorbital artery  **16.** middle meningeal artery  **17.** supraorbital vessels  **18.** superficial temporal artery

# THE ARTERIES OF THE BRAIN

The vertebral and internal carotid arteries anastomose as the circle of Willis at the base of the brain.

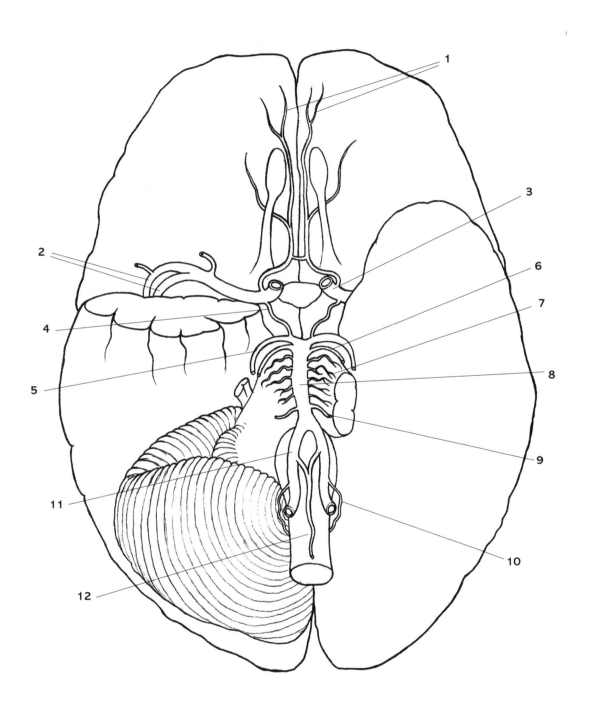

**Key: 1.** anterior cerebral artery  **2.** middle cerebral artery  **3.** internal carotid artery  **4.** posterior communicating artery  **5.** posterior cerebral artery  **6.** superior cerebellar artery  **7.** pontine branches  **8.** basilar artery  **9.** anterior inferior cerebellar artery  **10.** posterior inferior cerebellar artery  **11.** vertebral artery  **12.** anterior spinal artery

## HEAD AND NECK: DURAL VENOUS SINUSES

The venous sinuses of the cranium are spaces
between the layers of dura mater that are lined with
endothelium. They receive the veins of the brain
and drain to the internal jugular vein.

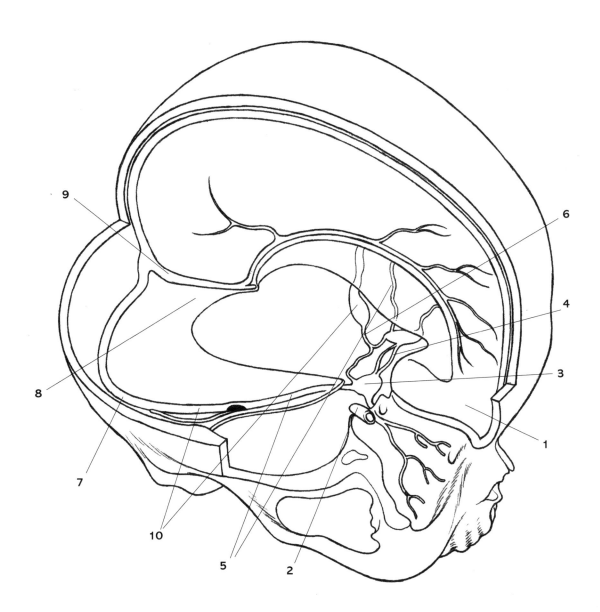

**Key: 1.** orbital plate of frontal bone  **2.** optic nerve  **3.** cavernous sinus  **4.** intercavernous sinus  **5.** superior petrosal
sinus  **6.** inferior petrosal sinus  **7.** transverse sinus  **8.** tentorium cerebelli  **9.** straight sinus  **10.** sigmoid sinus

# THORAX

The aorta is the main trunk of the general arterial system. It begins at the base of the left ventricle and runs upwards as the ascending aorta to the level of the second cartilage before curving downwards as the descending aorta through the thorax and abdomen, where it ends in front of the L4 vertebra as the common iliac arteries. The arch of the aorta gives three branches: right brachio-cephalic, left common carotid and left subclavian. In the thorax the descending aorta also gives the posterior intercostal arteries, the subcostal artery, the oesophagal artery and the bronchial arteries.

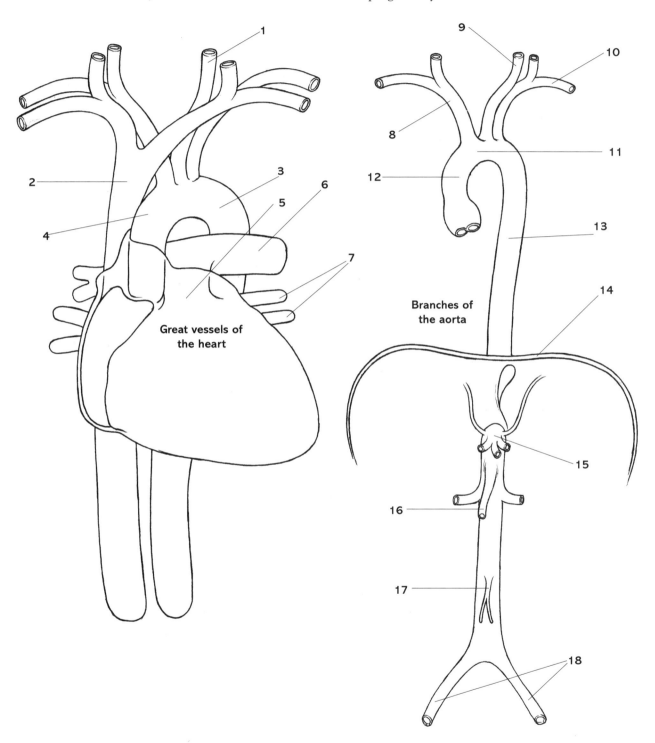

**Great vessels of the heart**

**Branches of the aorta**

Key: **1.** left common carotid artery  **2.** superior vena cava  **3.** arch of aorta  **4.** ascending aorta  **5.** pulmonary trunk  **6.** left pulmonary artery  **7.** pulmonary veins

**8.** right brachiocephalic artery  **9.** left common carotid artery  **10.** left subclavian artery  **11.** aortic arch **12.** ascending aorta  **13.** descending aorta  **14.** diaphragm  **15.** celiac trunk  **16.** superior mesenteric artery **17.** inferior mesenteric artery  **18.** common iliac arteries

## THE SURFACE ANATOMY OF THE HEART

The shape of the heart is that of an irregular, slightly flattened cone. It has a base, apex and three surfaces: sternocostal, diaphragmatic and pulmonary. The sternocostal (anterior) surface is limited by four borders, which are referred to as the borders of the heart, and consists chiefly of the right ventricle.

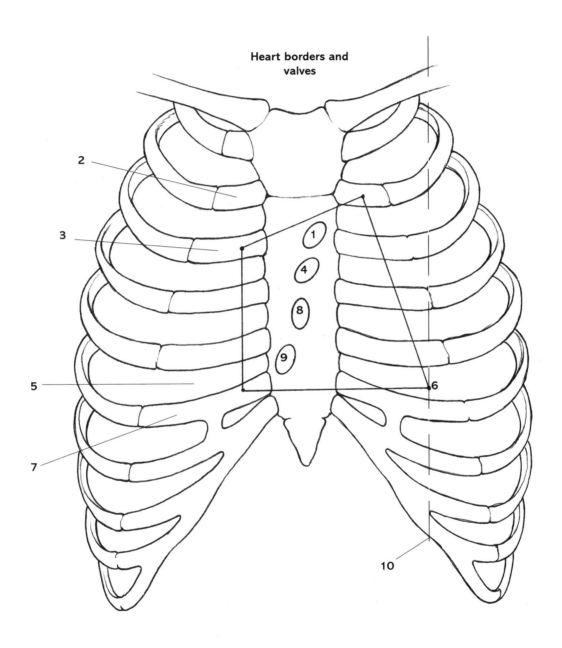

Heart borders and valves

**Key: 1.** pulmonary valve  **2.** second costal cartilage  **3.** third costal cartilage  **4.** aortic valve  **5.** fifth intercostal space  **6.** apex of the heart  **7.** sixth costal cartilage  **8.** mitral valve  **9.** tricuspid valve  **10.** midclavicular line

## SURFACE ANATOMY OF THE GREAT VESSELS

Two joints are useful in determining where the great vessels lie: the sternoclavicular and manubriosternal joints. Behind the sternoclavicular joints, the right brachiocephalic artery bifurcates into right common carotid and right subclavian arteries and the brachiocephalic veins form. Behind the manubriosternal joint the aortic arch begins and ends and the pulmonary trunk bifurcates into right and left pulmonary arteries.

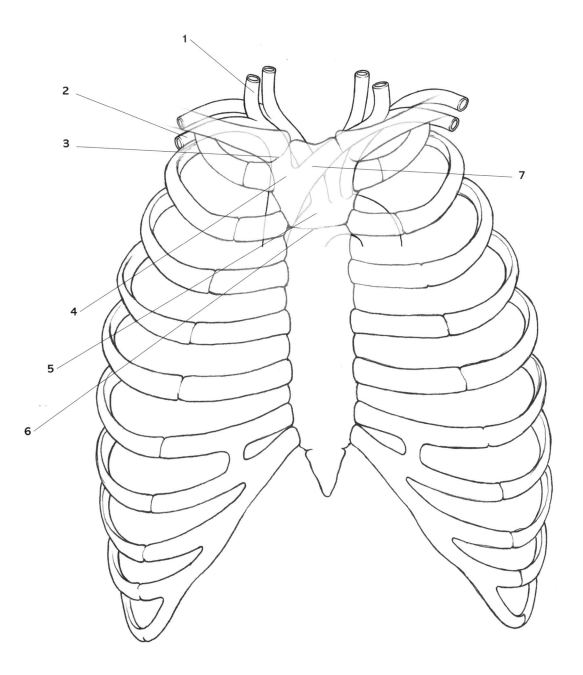

**Key: 1.** right internal jugular vein  **2.** subclavian vein  **3.** sternoclavicular joint  **4.** superior vena cava  **5.** aortic arch  **6.** manubriosternal joint  **7.** brachiocephalic vein

## ANTERIOR (STERNOCOSTAL) SURFACE OF HEART

The sternocostal (anterior) surface of the heart is directed upwards, forwards, and to the left. Its upper border is formed by the auricles of the atria, its right border by the right atrium, and its left border by the left ventricle.

## BASE OF THE HEART

The base of the heart is formed by the atria, almost entirely the left atrium, and is directed backwards. It is irregularly quadrilateral and receives the superior and inferior venae cavae into the right atrium and the pulmonary veins into the left.

The diaphragmatic surface sits on the central tendon of the diaphragm and is formed by the ventricles of the heart.

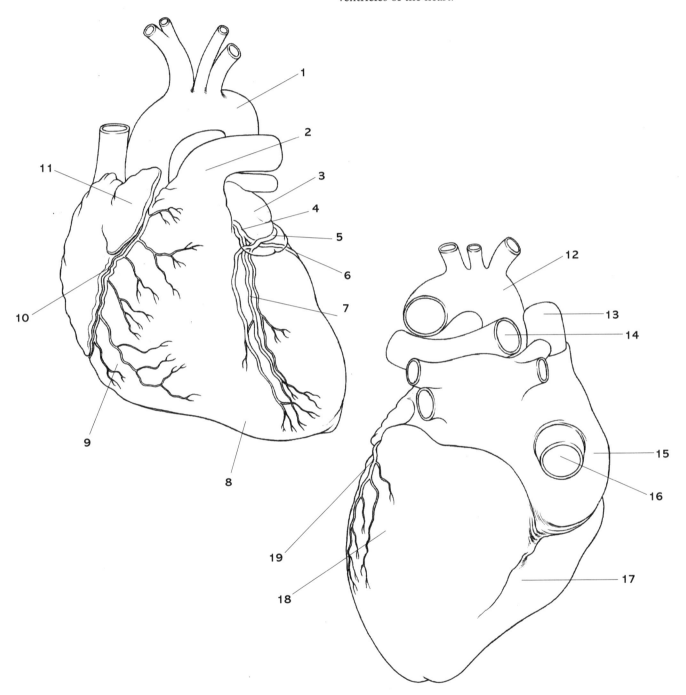

**Key: 1**. aorta  **2**. pulmonary trunk  **3**. left auricle (with left atrium behind)  **4**. left coronary artery  **5**. great cardiac vein  **6**. left marginal artery  **7**. anterior interventricular artery  **8**. left ventricle  **9**. right ventricle  **10**. right coronary artery  **11**. right auricle

**12**. aorta  **13**. superior vena cava  **14**. pulmonary artery  **15**. right atrium  **16**. inferior vena cava  **17**. right ventricle  **18**. left ventricle  **19**. left coronary artery

## HEART VALVES

A fibrocollagenous ring forms the 'skeleton of the heart' and is shown in the diagram below. This supports all four valves. It also separates the atria and ventricles physically and electrically and serves as a site of attachment for the myocardium. The valves that prevent backflow of blood are supported in the ventricles by the chordae tendinae. The chordae tendinae are shown on p.79.

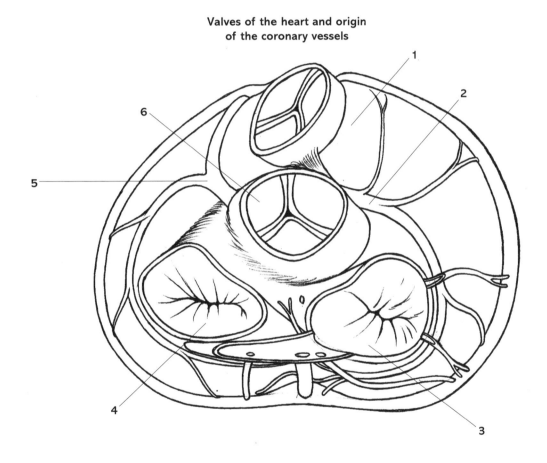

**Valves of the heart and origin
of the coronary vessels**

**Key: 1.** pulmonary valve  **2.** right coronary artery  **3.** tricuspid valve  **4.** mitral valve  **5.** left coronary artery
**6.** aortic valve

## INTERNAL FEATURES OF THE HEART

The atrial walls are lined by endocardium, except anteriorly and in the auricle, where pectinate muscle forms a series of small, vertical columns. The left and right atria are separated from each other by the interatrial septum. The mitral valve separates the left atrium and the left ventricle, and the tricuspid valve separates the right atrium from the right ventricle. The ventricles are separated from each other by the interventricular septum. The walls of the ventricles are lined by endocardium and are thrown into a series of ridges, called the trabeculae carneae, by papillary muscles. These muscles support the chordae tendinae.

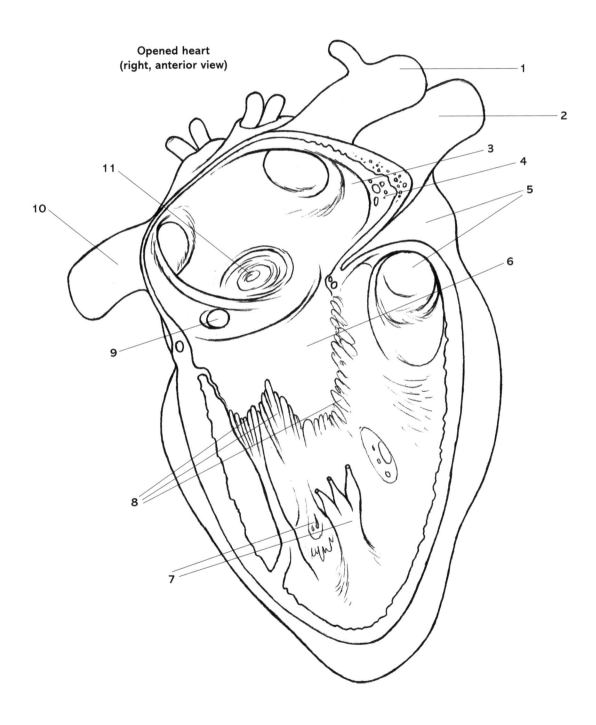

**Opened heart
(right, anterior view)**

**Key: 1.** superior vena cava  **2.** ascending aorta  **3.** right auricle  **4.** pectinate muscle  **5.** pulmonary trunk
**6.** tricuspid valve  **7.** papillary muscles  **8.** chordae tendinae  **9.** coronary valve  **10.** inferior vena cava
**11.** fossa ovalis

## ABDOMEN AND PELVIS

The abdominal aorta has three unpaired branches and three paired branches. The unpaired branches are as follows: the celiac trunk, which supplies structures derived from the embryonic foregut; the superior mesenteric branch, which supplies midgut structures; and the inferior mesenteric branch, which supplies the hindgut. The paired branches supply the adrenal glands, the kidneys via the renal arteries, and the gonads. The aorta bifurcates as the common iliac arteries, which, in turn, form the internal and external iliacs. The external iliac artery supplies the lower limbs, and the internal iliac artery supplies the pelvic viscera.

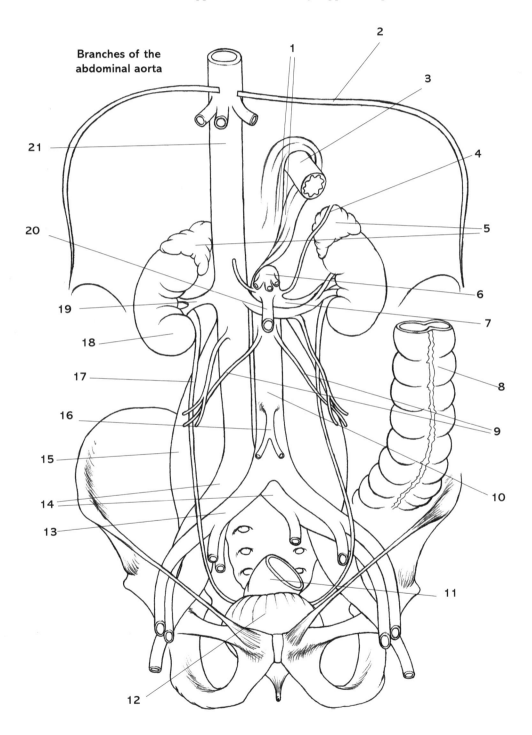

**Branches of the abdominal aorta**

Key: **1.** crus of diaphragm  **2.** diaphragm  **3.** oesophagus  **4.** suprarenal artery  **5.** suprarenal gland  **6.** celiac trunk  **7.** renal artery  **8.** descending colon  **9.** gonadal arteries  **10.** abdominal aorta  **11.** rectum  **12.** bladder  **13.** common iliac artery  **14.** common iliac vein  **15.** psoas major  **16.** inferior mesenteric artery  **17.** ureter  **18.** right kidney  **19.** renal vein  **20.** superior mesenteric artery  **21.** inferior vena cava

# THE LYMPHATIC SYSTEM

The lymphatic system consists of lymph, lymphatic vessels, lymphocytes, lymph nodes and lymphatic organs. This system interacts with two others: the circulatory (cardiovascular) system via the removal of excess interstitial fluid, and the immune system by proliferation, development and storage of immune cells.

Lymph is the interstitial (tissue) fluid that enters lymphatic vessels, and lymph nodes are organs that filter the lymph. Groups of lymph nodes are interspersed throughout the body, connected by a network of lymphatic vessels. The lymphatic vessels, unlike blood vessels, only carry fluid away from the tissues. Lymphatic tissue is reticular connective tissue that contains lymphocytes and other cells.

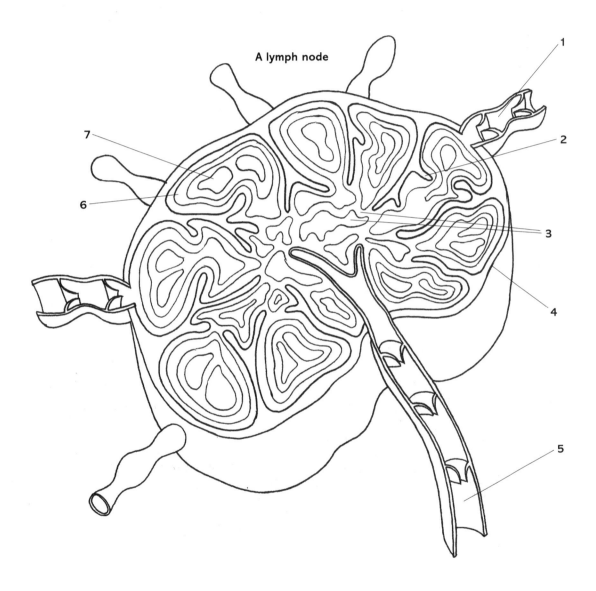

A lymph node

**Key: 1.** afferent lymphatic vessel  **2.** trabecula  **3.** medulla  **4.** capsule  **5.** efferent lymphatic vessels  **6.** lymphoid nodule  **7.** cortex

## OVERVIEW OF THE LYMPHATIC SYSTEM

The smallest lymphatic vessels are the lymph capillaries, which begin in the tissue spaces as blind-ended sacs. Lymph capillaries are found in all regions of the body, except for the bone marrow, central nervous system, and tissues that lack blood vessels, such as the epidermis.

Lymph capillaries merge to form lymphatic vessels. Small lymphatic vessels join to form larger tributaries. These are called lymphatic trunks, which drain large regions. Lymphatic trunks merge until the lymph enters the two lymphatic ducts. The right lymphatic duct drains lymph from the upper right quadrant of the body. The thoracic duct drains the rest of the body. The cisterna chyli is the commencement of the thoracic duct and receives lymph from the lower limb, pelvis and digestive tract.

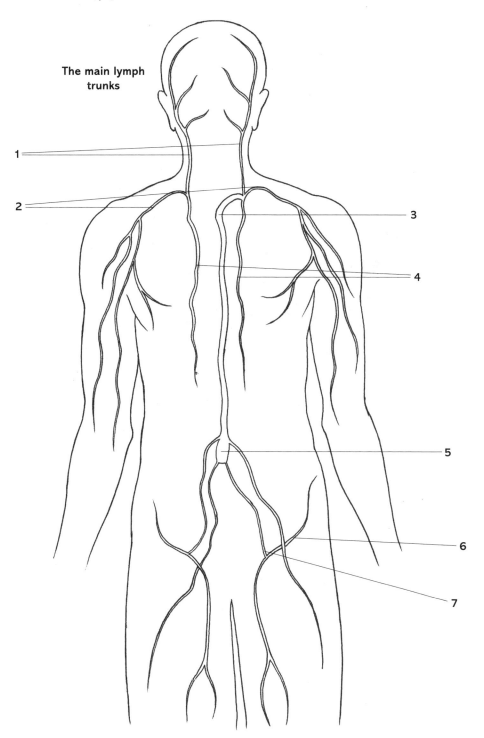

The main lymph trunks

Key: **1.** jugular lymph trunks  **2.** subclavian lymph trunks  **3.** thoracic duct  **4.** mediastinal lymph trunk
**5.** cisterna chyli  **6.** external iliac vessels  **7.** internal iliac vessels

## LYMPHATIC ORGANS

Lymphatic organs are characterised by clusters of lymphocytes and other cells, such as macrophages, enmeshed in a framework of short, branching connective tissue fibres. The lymphocytes originate in the red bone marrow with other blood cells and are carried in the blood from the bone marrow to the lymphatic organs. When the body is exposed to microorganisms and other foreign proteins, lymphocytes proliferate within the lymphatic organs and recognise and remove any invasion by that protein. These organs include the tonsils, spleen and thymus gland. Despite being a vestigial structure, the appendix contains a large amount of lymphatic tissue and is therefore capable of mounting an immune response.

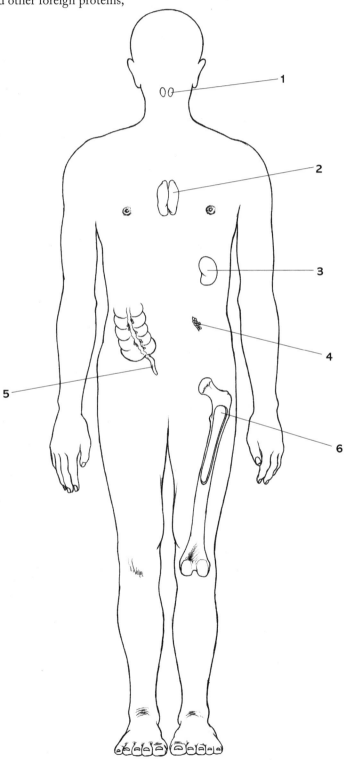

**Key: 1.** tonsils  **2.** thymus (in children)  **3.** spleen  **4.** Peyer's patches (on ileum)  **5.** appendix  **6.** bone marrow

## UPPER LIMB LYMPHATICS

In the upper limb, lymph from the skin and superficial fascia follows the superficial veins – cephalic and basilic. Lymph from deeper structures follows arteries. The cubital lymph nodes run alongside the basilic vein, proximal to the medial epicondyle of the humerus. They drain skin and subcutaneous tissues on the ulnar side of the hand and forearm, and themselves drain into the axillary lymph nodes.

**The upper limb lymph vessels and nodes**

**Key: 1.** infraclavicular nodes  **2.** apical nodes  **3.** central nodes  **4.** axillary lymphatic plexus  **5.** pectoral nodes
**6.** subscapular nodes  **7.** cephalic vein  **8.** humeral nodes  **9.** brachial lymph nodes  **10.** basilic vein
**11.** supratrochlear nodes  **12.** median cubital vein  **13.** cubital lymph nodes  **14.** palmar plexus

## Breast lymphatics

The axillary nodes are widely dispersed in the fat in the floor of the axilla; they are arranged as groups above and below the pectoralis minor tendon. These nodes drain the deep structures of the upper limb, the skin and fascia of the chest, and, importantly when considering metastatic spread, the breast.

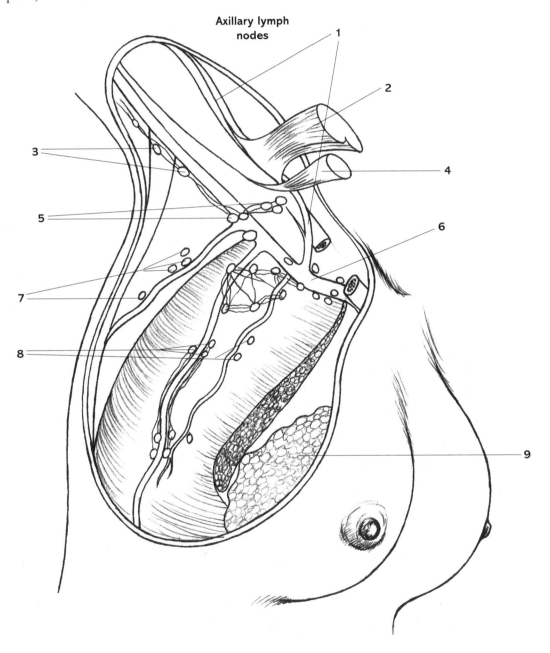

**Key: 1.** cephalic vein  **2.** pectoralis major  **3.** lateral axillary nodes  **4.** pectoralis minor  **5.** central axillary nodes
**6.** subclavian vein  **7.** posterior (subscapular) axillary nodes  **8.** anterior (pectoral) axillary nodes  **9.** breast tissue

## LYMPHATIC DRAINAGE OF THE LOWER LIMB

The superficial inguinal lymph nodes lie in the subcutaneous fat beneath the inguinal ligament and drain the skin and superficial tissue inferior to the umbilicus (except the region draining to popliteal nodes), including that of the external genitalia.

The deep nodes drain all deep structures of the lower limb and the superficial inguinal lymph nodes. The popliteal nodes drain the skin, and subcutaneous tissues are drained by the small saphenous vein and deep structures supplied by the popliteal artery.

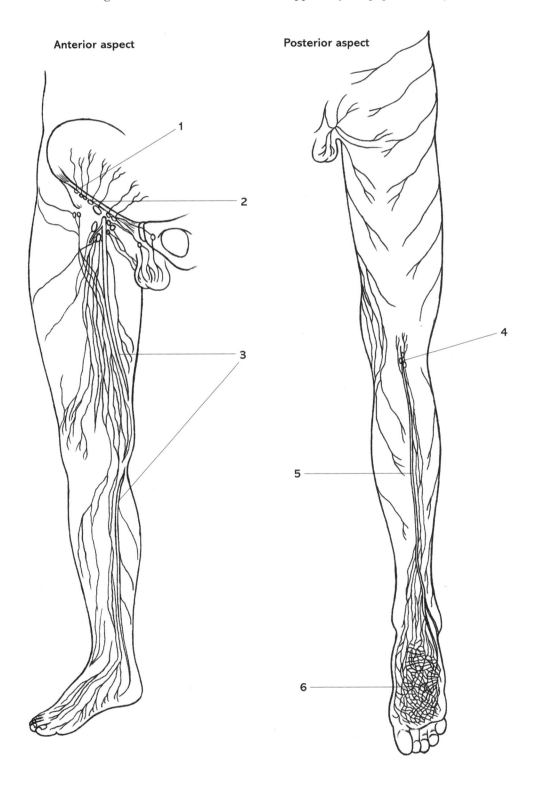

**Anterior aspect**

**Posterior aspect**

**Key: 1.** inguinal ligament **2.** superficial inguinal nodes **3.** great saphenous vein and lymphatic accompanying vessels **4.** popliteal lymph nodes **5.** small saphenous vein and accompanying vessels **6.** plantar plexus

## HEAD AND NECK LYMPHATICS

It is convenient to describe the lymphatics of the head and neck as a group that form a circle around the base of the skull and mandible and two chains running down the neck. The deep cervical chain of lymph nodes drain skin and subcutaneous tissues superior to the clavicle and all deep structures of head and neck (sometimes through intermediary groups of nodes, such as the preauricular, postauricular, occipital, submental and submandibular groups). The superficial cervical lymph nodes are the lower end of the preauricular (parotid) group; they are small and become conspicuous only when diseased. The 'circle' consists of submandibular, submental, preauricular, postauricular and occipital lymph nodes.

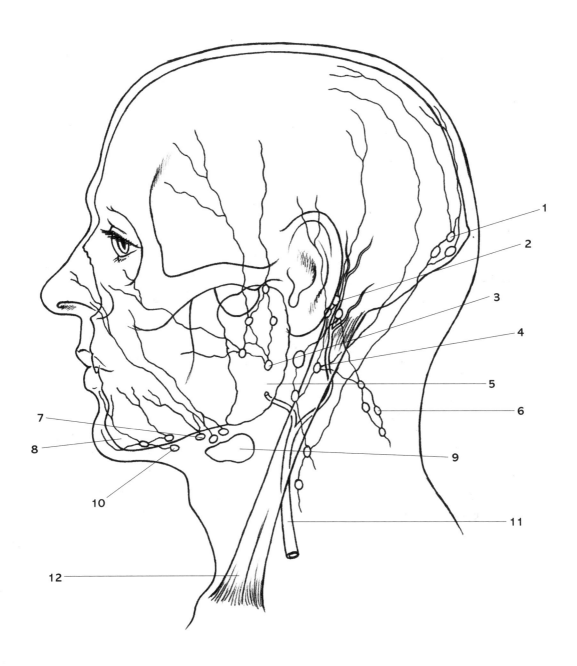

Key: **1.** occipital nodes **2.** postauricular nodes **3.** preauricular nodes **4.** deep cervical nodes **5.** parotid gland **6.** superficial cervical nodes **7.** submandibular nodes **8.** mandible **9.** submandibular gland **10.** submental nodes **11.** external jugular vein **12.** sternocleidomastoid muscle

## THORACIC LYMPHATICS

The terminal lymph vessels are the thoracic duct and the right lymphatic duct. Three vessels contribute to the right lymphatic duct: the right jugular, right subclavian and right bronchomediastinal lymph trunks. The right lymphatic duct drains into the right subclavian vein.

The thoracic duct drains all other lymph from the body. This duct commences in the abdomen as a dilated lymph channel, called the cisterna chyli. The cisterna chyli receives the intestinal, lumbar and intercostal trunks. Major groups of nodes in the thorax and abdomen include: the para-aortic (lumbar) nodes (which drain the common iliac nodes, deep structures supplied by parietal branches of abdominal aorta and sigmoid colon) and the anterior (superior) mediastinal nodes (which drain the heart, superior mediastinum and the pulmonary trunks, also draining the lung and tracheobronchial tree).

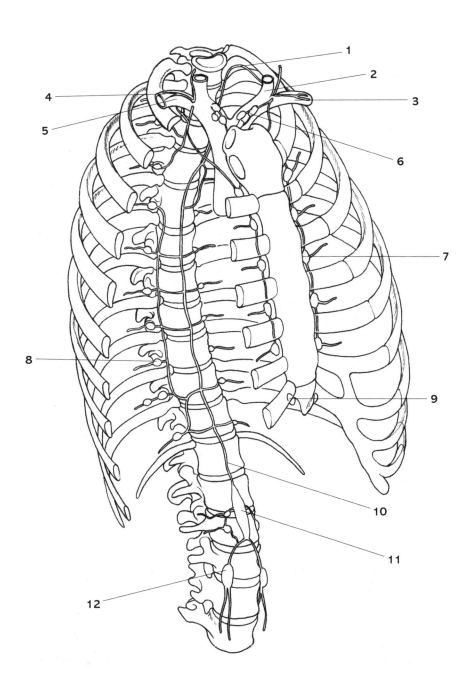

**Key: 1.** thoracic duct **2.** internal jugular vein **3.** left subclavian trunk **4.** right brachiocephalic vein **5.** right subclavian trunk **6.** brachiocephalic nodes **7.** parasternal nodes **8.** intercostal nodes **9.** diaphragmatic nodes **10.** thoracic duct **11.** cisterna chyli **12.** lateral aortic nodes

## ABDOMINAL LYMPHATICS

The cisterna chyli (feature 3) receives lymph from
the lower part of the body. Importantly, the cisterna
chyli receives fatty chyle from the intestines and so
is responsible for transporting the lipid products of
digestion.

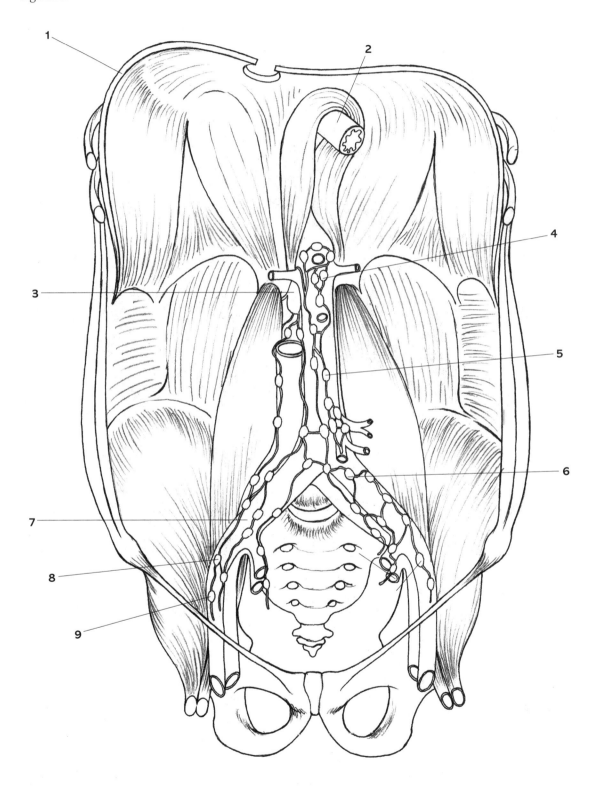

**Key: 1.** diaphragm  **2.** abdominal oesophagus  **3.** cisterna chyli  **4.** mesenteric nodes  **5.** aortic nodes
**6.** iliac nodes  **7.** common iliac artery  **8.** internal iliac nodes  **9.** external iliac nodes

# THE RESPIRATORY SYSTEM

Respiration refers both to the transport of gases to and from cells and to the biological processes of oxidation occurring within cells. The organs of the respiratory system lie in the head, neck and thorax. The upper respiratory tract comprises the nose with the nasal cavities, the paranasal sinuses, pharynx and larynx. The lower respiratory tract includes the trachea, the bronchi and the lungs,

where gaseous exchange occurs between air and blood. Inhaled air is cleaned, moistened and warmed during its passage through the respiratory tract. The nasal cavity and the larynx are separated by the oropharynx, where the respiratory and digestive tracts converge. This necessitates closure of the respiratory tract for short periods during swallowing.

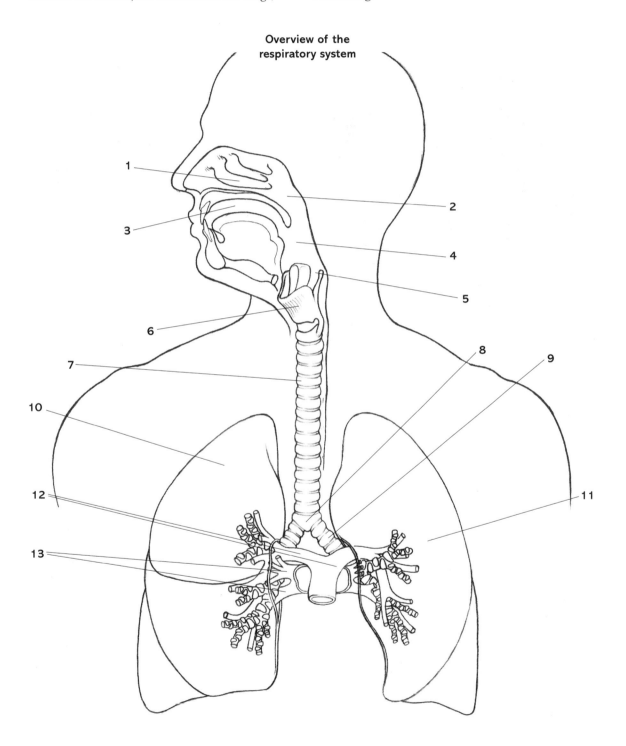

**Overview of the respiratory system**

**Key: 1.** nasal cavity  **2.** nasopharynx  **3.** oral cavity  **4.** oropharynx  **5.** laryngopharynx  **6.** larynx  **7.** trachea
**8.** carina  **9.** left main bronchus  **10.** right lung  **11.** left lung  **12.** pulmonary arteries  **13.** pulmonary veins

## THE NOSE

The external nose is separated from the lips and cheeks by the nasolabial fold. The nose is formed by the nasal bones, the alar cartilages and the lateral nasal cartilages. The nasal septum consists of a bony part, formed by the perpendicular plate of the ethmoid and the vomer, and a cartilaginous part. The nasal cavities are separated from each other by the septum and from the oral cavity by the palate. Each nasal cavity ends in a posterior nasal aperture (choana), which communicates with the nasopharynx. The floor of the nasal cavities is formed by the hard palate (composed of the maxilla and the palatine bone) and by the soft palate. The lateral wall has three projections: the superior, middle and inferior conchae. Below each concha lies the corresponding meatus.

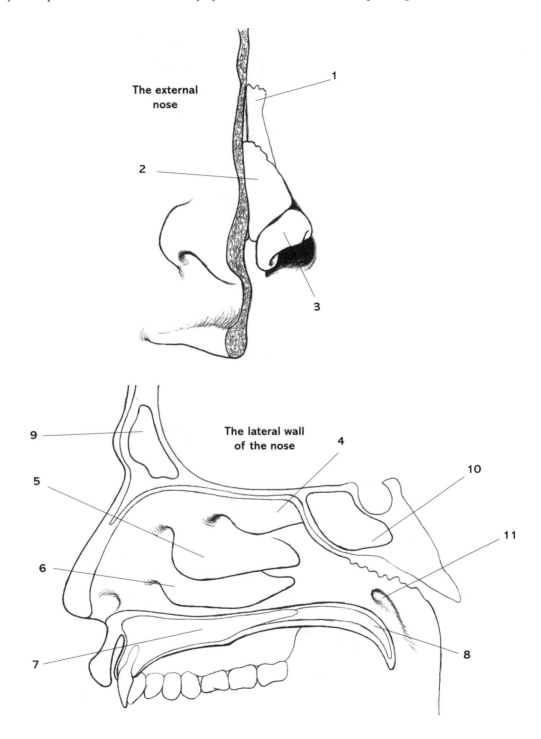

The external nose

The lateral wall of the nose

**Key: 1.** nasal bone  **2.** lateral nasal cartilage  **3.** major alar cartilage

**4.** superior concha  **5.** middle concha  **6.** inferior concha  **7.** hard palate  **8.** soft palate  **9.** frontal sinus
**10.** sphenoidal sinus  **11.** opening of Eustachian (auditory) tube

## THE PARANASAL SINUSES

The paranasal sinuses consist of four pairs of membrane-lined cavities within the facial bones: the frontal, maxillary, ethmoidal and sphenoidal sinuses. The frontal sinuses lie above the orbit and drain into the middle meatus on the lateral wall of the nose. The maxillary sinuses lie laterally and drain into the middle meatus. The ethmoidal sinuses lie between the orbit and the nose.

They comprise the anterior and middle air cells, which open into the middle meatus, and the posterior ethmoidal air cells, which open into the superior meatus. The sphenoidal sinuses open into the sphenoethmoidal recess above the superior concha. The sinuses are thought to act as resonance chambers during speech and may also lighten the bones of the facial skeleton.

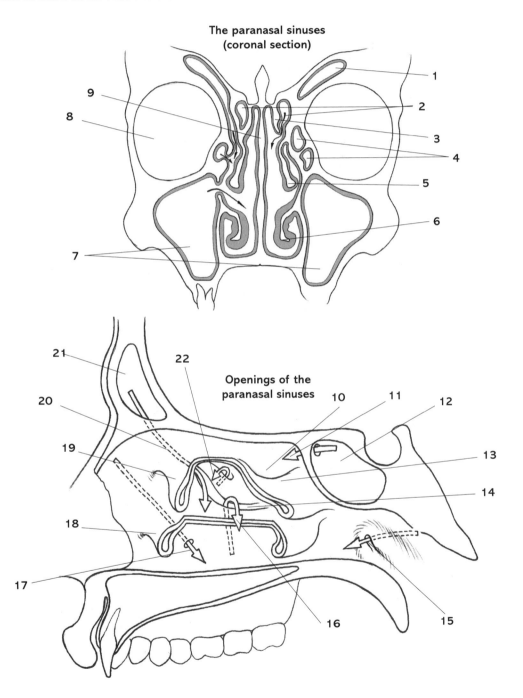

The paranasal sinuses
(coronal section)

Openings of the
paranasal sinuses

Key: 1. frontal sinus  2. posterior ethmoidal sinuses  3. superior concha  4. anterior ethmoidal sinuses  5. middle concha  6. inferior concha  7. maxillary sinuses  8. orbit  9. nasal septum

10. superior concha  11. opening of sphenoidal sinus  12. sphenoidal sinus  13. opening of posterior ethmoidal sinuses  14. hiatus semilunaris  15. opening of Eustachian (auditory) tube  16. opening of maxillary sinus  17. opening of nasolacrimal duct  18. inferior concha  19. middle concha  20. opening of frontal and anterior ethmoidal sinuses  21. frontal sinus  22. opening of middle ethmoidal sinuses (onto ethmoidal bulla)

# CARTILAGES AND MEMBRANES OF THE LARYNX

The larynx guards the entrance to the lower respiratory tract. It is composed of cartilages, ligaments and muscles. The foundation of the laryngeal skeleton is the cricoid cartilage, which is shaped like a signet ring. It articulates with the arytenoid cartilages superiorly and with the thyroid cartilage laterally. The epiglottis is a leaf-shaped structure formed of yellow elastic cartilage, with its inferior process attaching in the midline below the superior thyroid notch. The larynx is suspended from the hyoid bone by the thyrohyoid membrane. The cricothyroid membrane extends between the internal aspects of the cricoid and thyroid cartilages, while the quadrangular membrane connects the arytenoid cartilages and the epiglottis.

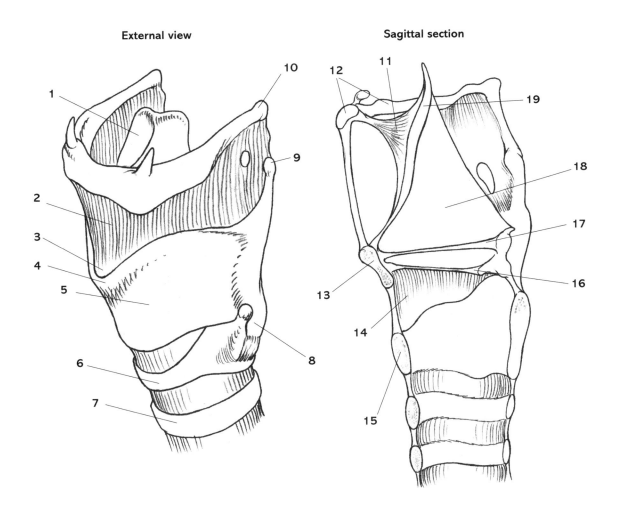

**External view**

**Sagittal section**

**Key: 1.** epiglottis **2.** thyrohyoid membrane **3.** superior thyroid notch **4.** laryngeal prominence ('Adam's apple') **5.** thyroid cartilage **6.** cricoid cartilage **7.** tracheal ring **8.** inferior horn of thyroid cartilage **9.** superior horn of thyroid cartilage **10.** hyoid bone (with greater and lesser horns)

**11.** hyoepiglottic ligament **12.** hyoid bone **13.** thyroid cartilage **14.** cricothyroid membrane ('conus elasticus') **15.** cricoid cartilage **16.** vocal fold ('true cord') **17.** vestibular fold ('false cord') **18.** quadrangular membrane **19.** epiglottis

## MUSCLES OF THE LARYNX

The intrinsic muscles of the larynx can be divided into three groups, according to their functions. The laryngeal inlet is closed and opened by the aryepiglotticus and the thyroepiglotticus respectively. The vocal folds (cords) are opened (abducted) by the posterior cricoarytenoid and closed (adducted) by the lateral cricoarytenoid and interarytenoids. When the cords are closed in phonation, the cricothyroid lengthens them (raising the pitch) and the thyroarytenoid shortens them (lowering the pitch). The quality of the voice relies on the precise balance of activity in all the intrinsic muscles. All these muscles are supplied by the recurrent laryngeal nerve, except for the cricothyroid, which is supplied by the external branch of the superior laryngeal nerve.

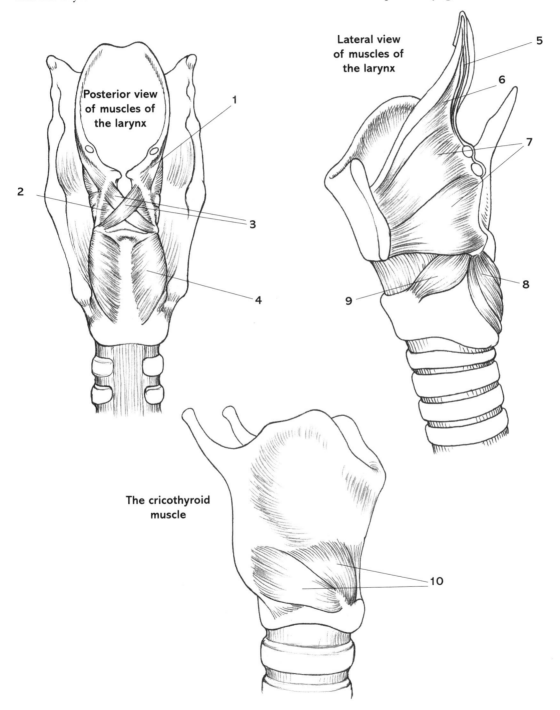

Posterior view of muscles of the larynx

Lateral view of muscles of the larynx

The cricothyroid muscle

**Key: 1.** aryepiglotticus  **2.** transverse fibres of interarytenoids  **3.** oblique fibres of interarytenoids  **4.** posterior cricoarytenoid

**5.** aryepiglotticus  **6.** thyroepiglotticus  **7.** thyroarytenoid  **8.** posterior cricoarytenoid  **9.** lateral cricoarytenoid  **10.** cricothyroid muscle

## INTERIOR OF THE LARYNX

The interior of the larynx is divided by the vocal folds into supraglottic and infraglottic parts. The supraglottic part consists of the vestibule, which extends from the laryngeal opening to the vestibular folds ('false cords'). The fossa between the vestibular and vocal folds ('true cords') is the ventricle, the anterior part of which extends upwards to form a pouch (saccule). The space between the vocal folds is the glottis, which extends posteriorly between the arytenoid cartilages (rima glottidis). The infraglottic part widens towards the cricoid cartilage and is continuous with the trachea inferiorly. The vocal folds are covered by stratified squamous epithelium; the rest of the larynx is covered by respiratory epithelium (pseudostratified ciliated columnar).

**Coronal section**

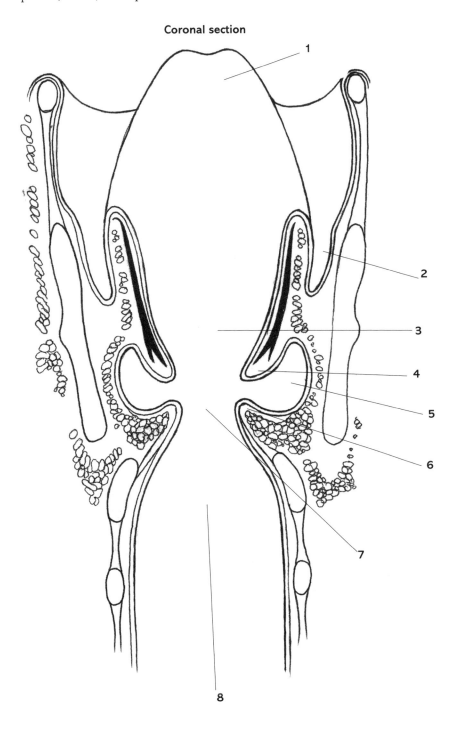

**Key: 1.** epiglottis  **2.** piriform recess  **3.** vestibule  **4.** vestibular fold ('false cord')  **5.** ventricle  **6.** vocal fold ('true cord')  **7.** rima glottidis  **8.** infraglottic cavity

## THE TRACHEA AND BRONCHIAL TREE

The trachea extends from the cricoid cartilage into the thorax, where it divides into left and right main bronchi at the carina. Embedded in its connective tissue wall are C-shaped cartilaginous rings. The posterior free edges are connected by the trachealis muscle, which contracts to reduce the tracheal diameter. The aortic arch curves over the left main bronchus, while the pulmonary trunk divides into the two pulmonary arteries anteriorly. The main bronchi divide into lobar bronchi that give segmental bronchi. These undergo further division to give small bronchi, which give rise to bronchioles, terminal bronchioles, and, finally, to respiratory bronchioles, the walls of which are interrupted by thin-walled sacs called alveoli, where gaseous exchange occurs.

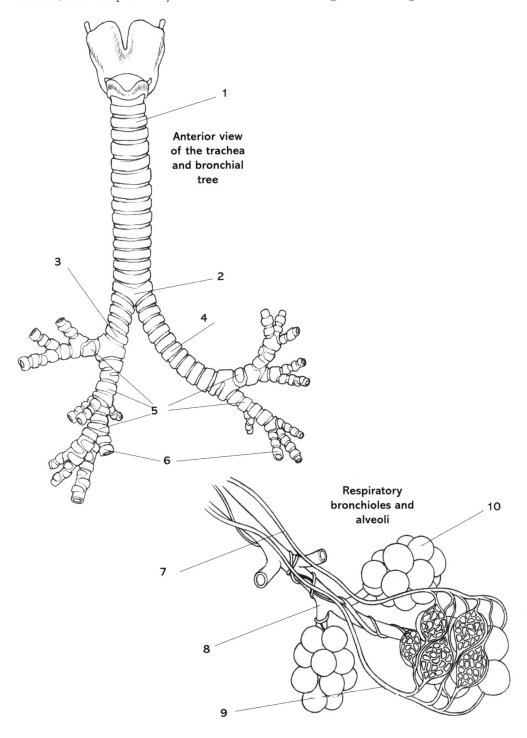

Anterior view of the trachea and bronchial tree

Respiratory bronchioles and alveoli

Key: **1.** trachea **2.** carina **3.** right main bronchus **4.** left main bronchus **5.** lobar bronchi **6.** segmental bronchi

**7.** arteriole (from pulmonary artery) **8.** respiratory bronchiole **9.** postcapillary vein (to pulmonary vein) **10.** alveolus

## THE PLEURAL CAVITIES AND LUNGS

The lungs are covered with pleurae, which comprise visceral and parietal layers. Each pleura extends above the medial end of the clavicle for about 2.5cm (1in), meets its fellow at the manubriosternal joint, and runs to the level of the fourth costal cartilage, where the left diverges. The pleurae cross the midclavicular and midaxillary lines at the level of the eighth and tenth costal cartilages respectively, reaching the neck of the twelfth rib posteriorly. The surface markings of the lungs coincide with the pleural markings, except posteriorly, where they are two rib spaces higher. The right lung has three lobes (upper, middle and lower) and two fissures (oblique and transverse). On the left, the oblique fissure divides the lung into upper and lower lobes.

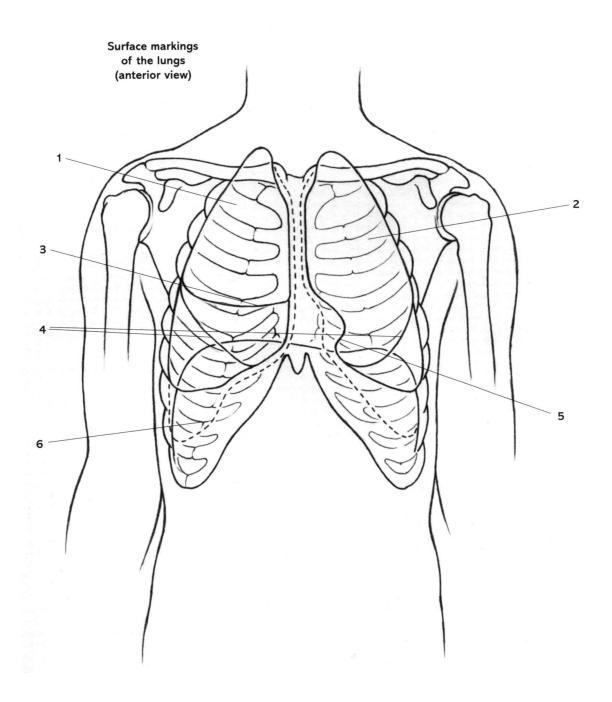

**Surface markings of the lungs (anterior view)**

Key: **1.** right lung  **2.** left lung  **3.** horizontal fissure  **4.** oblique fissures  **5.** cardiac notch  **6.** outline of parietal pleura

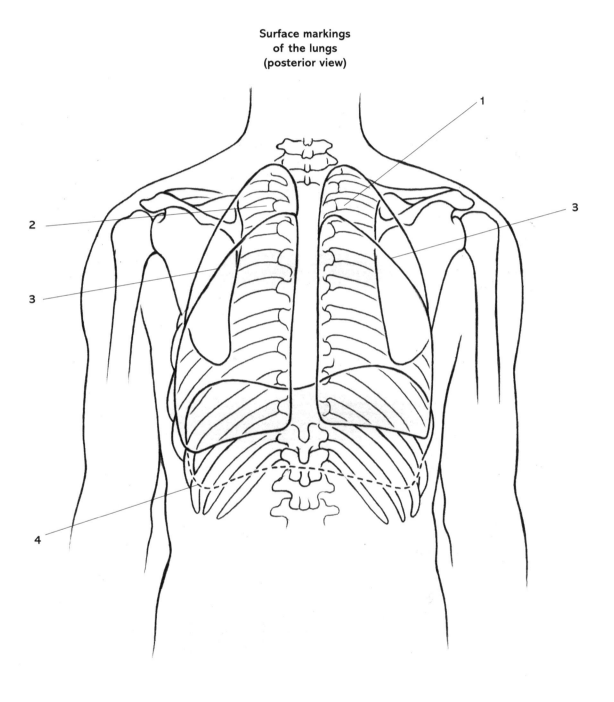

**Surface markings
of the lungs
(posterior view)**

**Key: 1.** right lung  **2.** left lung  **3.** oblique fissure  **4.** outline of parietal pleura

## THE PLEURAL CAVITIES AND LUNGS

Each lung is cone-shaped, with its base lying inferiorly on the diaphragm. The mediastinal (medial) surface is concave and corresponds to the convex pericardial surface. The structures at each hilum include a bronchus lying posteriorly, pulmonary arteries anteriorly, pulmonary veins anteroinferiorly and lymph nodes. As the right main bronchus is shorter, the upper lobe bronchus may also be seen. On the left, the lung is related to the left ventricle, aortic arch and descending aorta. On the right, the lung is related to the right atrium, the superior vena cava with the azygos arch entering it, the brachiocephalic trunk and the trachea. The oesophagus lies posteriorly on both sides.

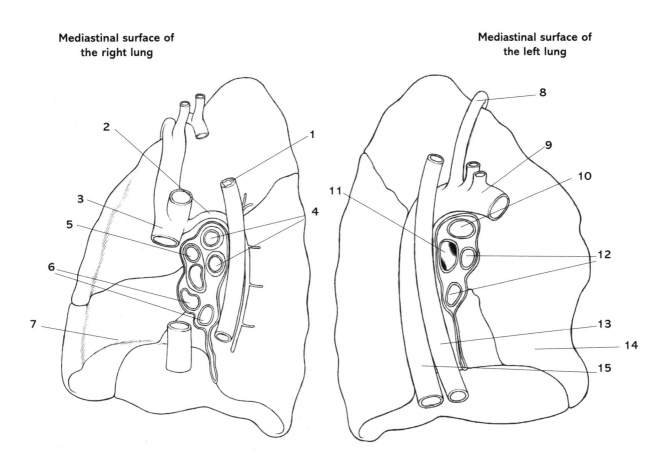

**Mediastinal surface of the right lung**

**Mediastinal surface of the left lung**

**Key: 1.** oesophagus  **2.** azygos vein  **3.** superior vena cava  **4.** right main bronchus and upper lobe bronchus
**5.** pulmonary artery  **6.** pulmonary veins  **7.** right atrium

**8.** left subclavian artery  **9.** arch of aorta  **10.** pulmonary artery  **11.** left main bronchus  **12.** pulmonary veins
**13.** oesophagus  **14.** left ventricle  **15.** descending aorta

# THE DIGESTIVE SYSTEM

Digestion is the process whereby food is converted into substances that can be absorbed and assimilated by the body. The digestive system extends from the mouth to the anus and includes the liver and the pancreas. The organs involved are located in the head, neck and trunk and are derived embryologically from the foregut, midgut and hindgut. The component parts of the digestive system are the oral cavity, pharynx, oesophagus, stomach, small intestine (duodenum, jejunum and ileum), large intestine (colon) and rectum. Accessory organs include the liver, which plays a vital role in digestion and detoxification; the gall bladder, which stores and concentrates bile; and the pancreas, which secretes digestive enzymes.

**Overview of the digestive system**

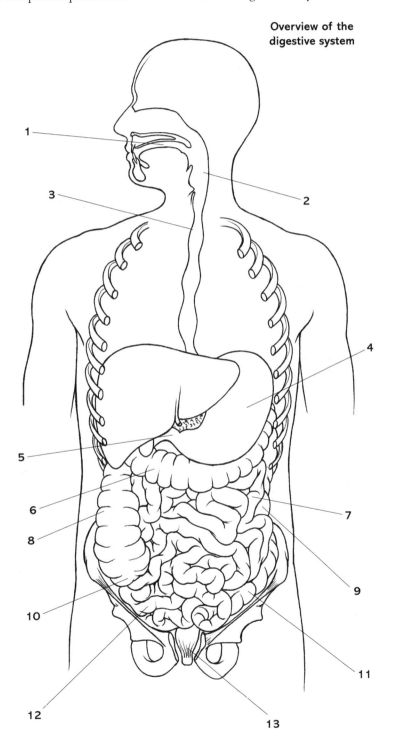

**Key: 1.** oral cavity  **2.** pharynx  **3.** oesophagus  **4.** stomach  **5.** duodenum  **6.** transverse colon  **7.** jejunum  **8.** ascending colon  **9.** descending colon  **10.** caecum  **11.** sigmoid colon  **12.** ileum  **13.** rectum

## THE ORAL CAVITY

The oral cavity is the first part of the digestive tract, and opens onto the exterior through the lips. The outer part of the mouth is the vestibule, which lies between the lips, cheeks, teeth and gums. Between the lip and the gums is a vertical midline upper and lower mucosal fold called the frenulum. The parotid duct opens into the vestibule opposite the second upper molar tooth.

The inner part of the mouth is the actual oral cavity, which is bounded anteriorly and laterally by the teeth and the gums, with the palate as the roof and the tongue as its floor. The submandibular duct opens onto the sublingual papilla, and the ducts of the sublingual gland open onto the sublingual fold or into the submandibular duct.

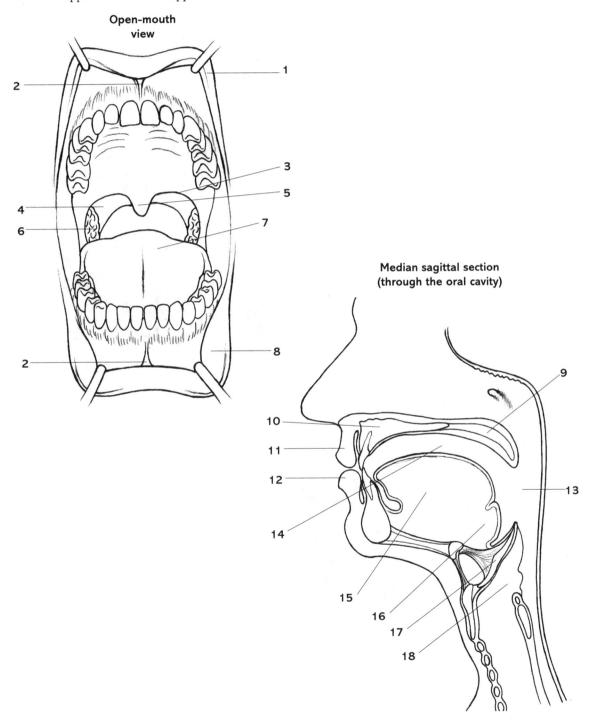

**Open-mouth view**

**Median sagittal section (through the oral cavity)**

**Key: 1.** upper lip  **2.** frenulum  **3.** palatoglossal folds  **4.** palatopharyngeal folds  **5.** uvula  **6.** palatine tonsils  **7.** tongue  **8.** lower lip

**9.** soft palate  **10.** hard palate  **11.** upper lip  **12.** lower lip  **13.** pharynx  **14.** oral cavity  **15.** tongue  **16.** root of the tongue  **17.** epiglottis  **18.** laryngeal inlet

## THE TEETH

There are 20 deciduous (milk) teeth, with five in each quadrant: two incisors, one canine and two molars. There are 32 permanent teeth, with eight in each quadrant: two incisors, one canine, two premolars and three molars. The incisors are chisel-shaped for biting; the long canines are for tearing and gripping; the premolars are for grinding and crushing; and the molars are mainly for chewing. A tooth consists of a pulp cavity surrounded by dentine, with a foramen at the apex of the root that transmits blood vessels, lymphatics and nerves. The crown extends above the gingiva and is covered by enamel. The tooth is held in its socket by the periodontal membrane, which unites the bone to the cement covering the root.

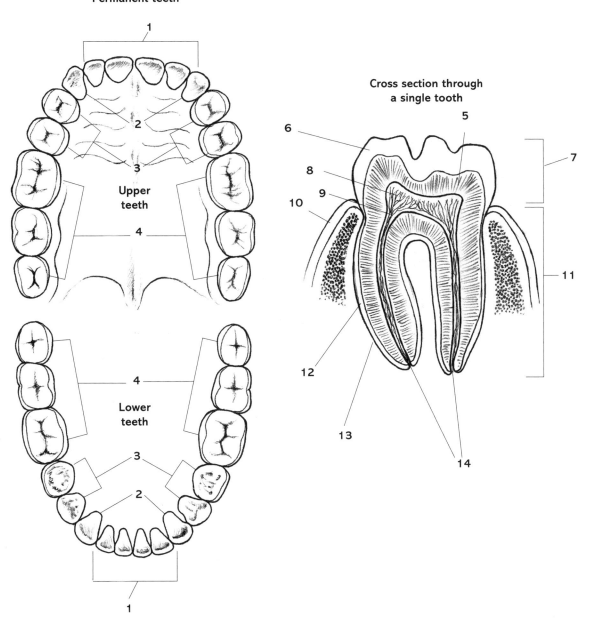

**Permanent teeth**

Upper teeth

Lower teeth

**Cross section through a single tooth**

**Key: 1.** incisors  **2.** canines  **3.** premolars  **4.** molars

**5.** dentine  **6.** enamel  **7.** crown  **8.** nerve plexus  **9.** pulp  **10.** gingiva  **11.** root  **12.** cementum  **13.** periodontal membrane  **14.** apex

## THE TONGUE

The tongue is important for chewing, sucking and tasting. The extrinsic muscles connect it to the mandible, palate, hyoid and styloid process, altering its position and shape. The intrinsic muscles alter its shape. The hypoglossal nerve supplies all the muscles, except the palatoglossus. On the dorsum, vallate papillae mark the junction of the anterior two thirds and posterior one third.

The terminal sulcus leads back to the foramen caecum. Fungiform and vallate papillae have taste buds. The posterior one third consists of lymphoid tissue. The lingual nerve mediates general sensation, and the chorda tympani mediates taste from the anterior two thirds, while the glossopharyngeal nerve mediates general sensation and taste from the posterior one third.

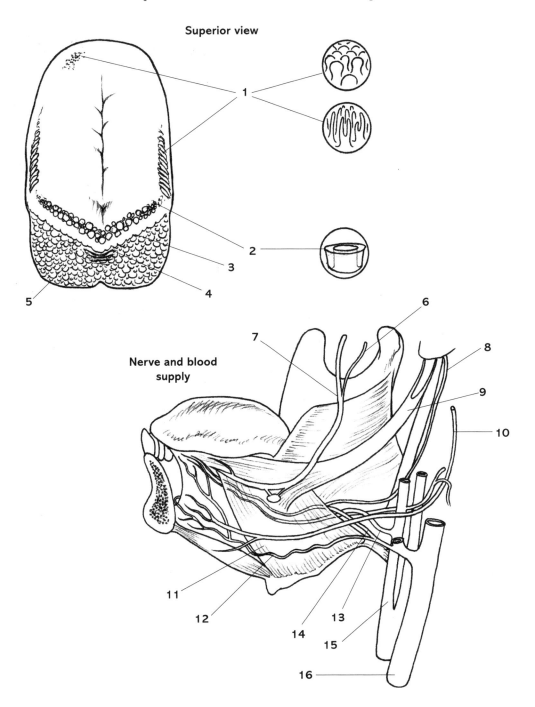

**Superior view**

**Nerve and blood supply**

**Key: 1.** dorsum (with fungiform and filiform papillae) **2.** vallate papillae **3.** terminal sulcus **4.** foramen caecum **5.** lingual follicles

**6.** chorda tympani (from VII) **7.** lingual nerve (Vc) **8.** glossopharyngeal nerve (IX) **9.** styloglossus **10.** hypoglossal nerve (XII) **11.** hyoglossus **12.** deep lingual vein **13.** lingual artery **14.** dorsal lingual vein **15.** external carotid artery **16.** internal jugular vein

## THE SALIVARY GLANDS

The parotid gland is the largest salivary gland. It lies anterior to the ear on the ramus of the mandible. Its duct crosses the masseter and pierces the buccinator to open into the vestibule of the mouth. It is covered by parotid fascia. The submandibular gland lies between the mandible and the bellies of the digastric. Its deep lobe passes with the duct around the posterior border of the mylohyoid to open at the base of the lingual frenulum. The sublingual gland lies on mylohyoid, forming the sublingual fold. There are numerous sublingual ducts, most of which open directly into the oral cavity. The larger sublingual duct opens into or adjacent to the submandibular duct.

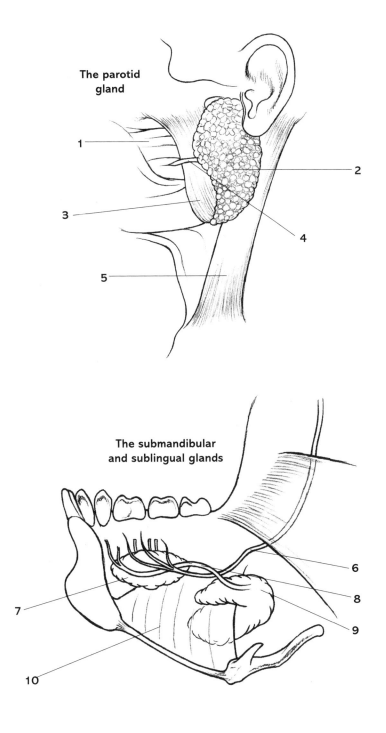

Key:  **1.** buccinator  **2.** parotid gland  **3.** masseter  **4.** parotid duct  **5.** sternocleidomastoid
**6.** lingual nerve  **7.** sublingual gland  **8.** submandibular duct  **9.** submandibular gland (deep and superficial parts)
**10.** mylohyoid

## THE PHARYNX

The pharynx is a musculomembranous tube that is around 12cm (5in) long, attached to the base of the skull and continuous with the oesophagus. It comprises the nasopharynx, which is part of the respiratory tract and is always patent; the oropharynx, which is continuous with the mouth; and the laryngopharynx, which opens on swallowing. The muscles consist of three constrictors (superior, middle and inferior), as well as the stylopharyngeus, salpingopharyngeus and palatopharyngeus. The auditory tubes open onto the lateral wall of the nasopharynx. The valleculae lie between the base of the tongue and the epiglottis in the oropharynx. In the larynopharynx, the piriform fossae lie between the laryngeal inlet and the pharyngeal side wall.

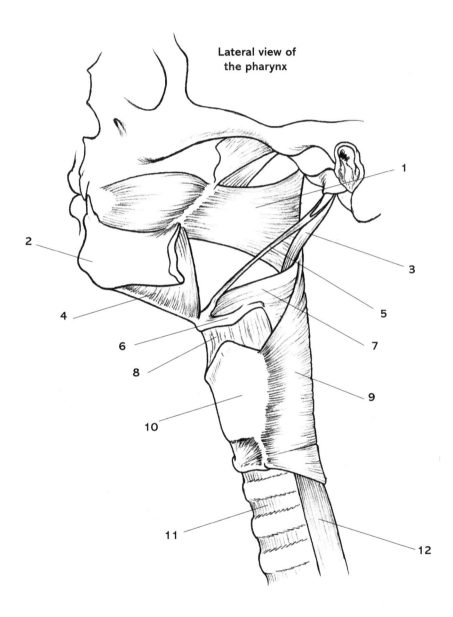

Lateral view of the pharynx

**Key: 1.** superior constrictor  **2.** mandible  **3.** stylopharyngeus  **4.** mylohyoid  **5.** stylohyoid ligament  **6.** hyoid bone
**7.** middle constrictor  **8.** thyrohyoid membrane  **9.** inferior constrictor  **10.** larynx  **11.** trachea  **12.** oesophagus

**Internal features of the pharnyx
(posterior view with pharyngeal
wall opened)**

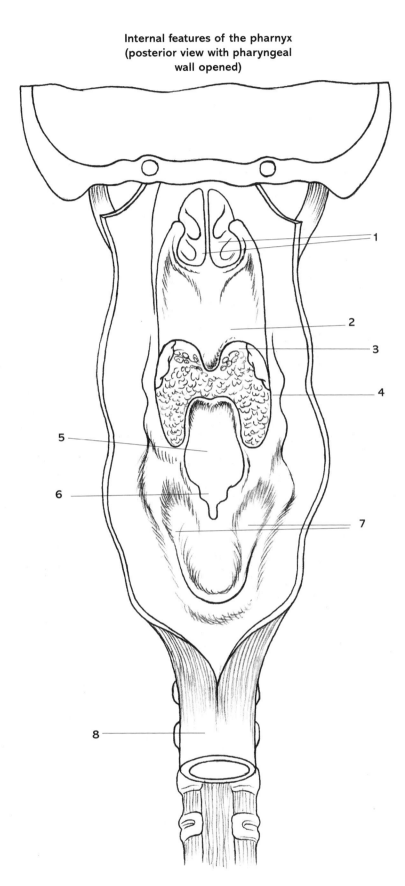

**Key: 1.** nasal choanae  **2.** soft palate  **3.** oropharyngeal isthmus  **4.** palatopharyngeal fold  **5.** epiglottis  **6.** laryngeal inlet  **7.** piriform fossae  **8.** oesophagus

# THE OESOPHAGUS

The oesophagus is around 25cm (10in) long and conveys the bolus of food from the pharynx to the stomach. It begins at the lower border of the cricoid cartilage at the level of the sixth cervical vertebra and passes through the oesophagal hiatus in the diaphragm at the level of the tenth thoracic vertebra. There are three 'natural' constrictions: at the cricopharyngeus (upper oesophageal sphincter); the aortic or bronchial narrowing, where the oesophagus lies posterior to the aortic arch and the tracheal bifurcation; and the diaphragmatic narrowing. The upper one third of the oesophagus is composed of striated muscle, which is gradually replaced by smooth muscle in the lower two thirds. The lower one third is a site of portosystemic anastomoses.

**Key: 1.** pharynx  **2.** 'natural constriction' at cricopharyngeus  **3.** oesophagus  **4.** trachea  **5.** 'natural constriction' at aortic/bronchial narrowing  **6.** right and left main bronchi  **7.** aortic arch  **8.** 'natural constriction' at the oesophageal hiatus  **9.** diaphragm

# THE STOMACH

The stomach is involved in both chemical and mechanical digestion of food and discharges chyme intermittently into the duodenum. It has the following parts: cardia (continuous with the oesophagus), fundus (above the cardia on the left), body, antrum, and pylorus. The lesser curvature is attached to the lesser omentum, and the greater curvature to the greater omentum. Anteriorly, it is related to the diaphragm, the abdominal wall and the inferior surface of the liver. Posteriorly, it is separated from the pancreas by the lesser sac. The shape of the stomach varies with its contents and body posture, and it has a capacity of around 1.4 litres (2.5pts). The muscle layer consists of bundles of smooth muscle fibres, with circular fibres forming the pyloric sphincter.

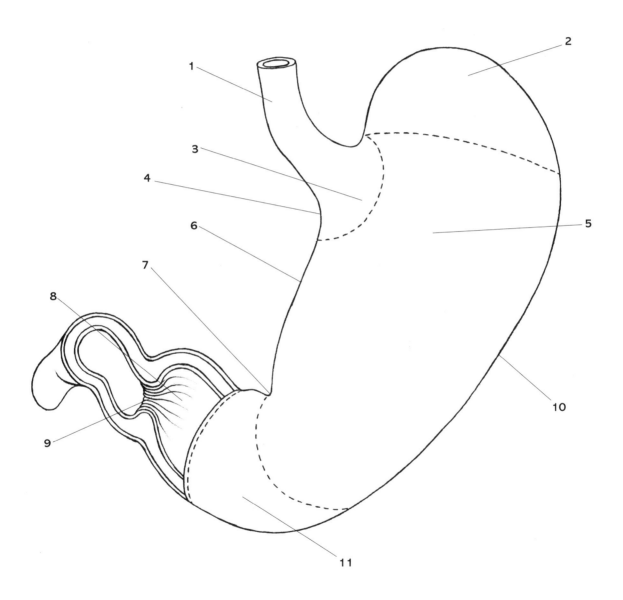

**Key: 1.** abdominal oesophagus  **2.** fundus  **3.** cardia  **4.** gastro-oesophageal junction  **5.** body  **6.** lesser curvature  **7.** angular notch  **8.** pyloric canal  **9.** pyloric sphincter  **10.** greater curvature  **11.** antrum

## THE LIVER

The liver is the largest gland in the body, weighing around 1.5kg (3 pounds 5 ounces). It lies under the costal margin in the right hypochondrium and extends to the left hypochondrium. It is associated with the falciform ligament (containing the ligamentum teres), the right and left triangular ligaments, the coronary ligament and the ligamentum venosum. The fissure for the ligamentum teres divides the liver into left and right lobes, with the latter being subdivided into the quadrate and caudate lobes. The porta hepatis is the point of entry for the portal vein and the hepatic artery and for the exit of the right and left hepatic ducts to form the common bile duct with the cystic duct. The fossa for the gallbladder lies on the inferior surface of the right lobe.

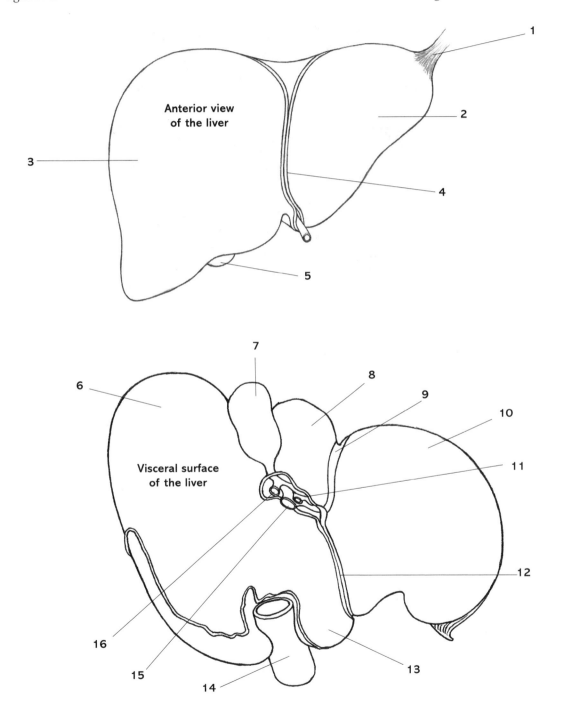

**Key: 1.** left triangular ligament  **2.** left lobe  **3.** right lobe  **4.** falciform ligament  **5.** gallbladder

**6.** right lobe  **7.** gallbladder  **8.** quadrate lobe  **9.** fissure for ligamentum teres  **10.** left lobe  **11.** hepatic artery  **12.** fissure for ligamentum venosum  **13.** caudate lobe  **14.** inferior vena cava   **15.** portal vein  **16.** common bile duct

## THE BILIARY TREE

The duodenum is around 25cm (10in) long. It is
mostly retroperitoneal and forms a C-shaped
bend around the head of the pancreas. It is divided
into four parts: superior, descending, inferior
(horizontal) and ascending. The common bile
duct joins the main pancreatic duct and opens at
the duodenal papilla (ampulla of Vater) on the
posteromedial wall of the second part of the
duodenum, where the sphincter of Oddi is present.

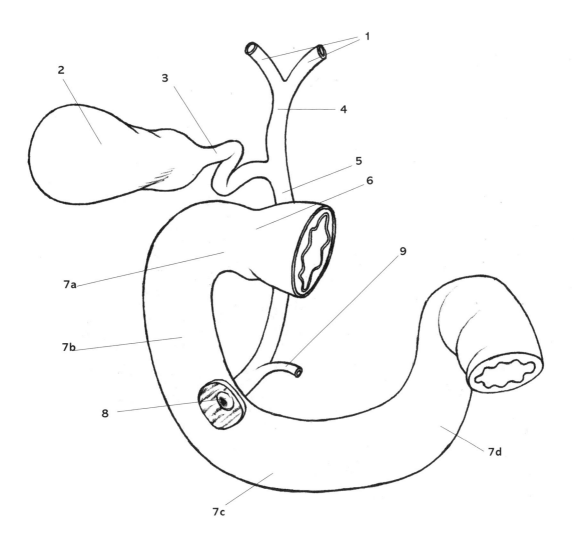

**Key: 1.** right and left hepatic ducts  **2.** gallbladder  **3.** cystic duct  **4.** common hepatic duct  **5.** common bile duct
**6.** pylorus  **7a–d.** superior (a), descending (b), inferior (c) and ascending (d) parts of duodenum  **8.** duodenal
papilla  **9.** main pancreatic duct

## THE PANCREAS

The pancreas is a retroperitoneal structure lying
curved across the vertebral column, with a head,
uncinate process, neck, body and tail. It secretes
digestive enzymes into the duodenum via the
pancreatic duct. The accessory pancreatic duct
opens proximal to the major duodenal papilla.

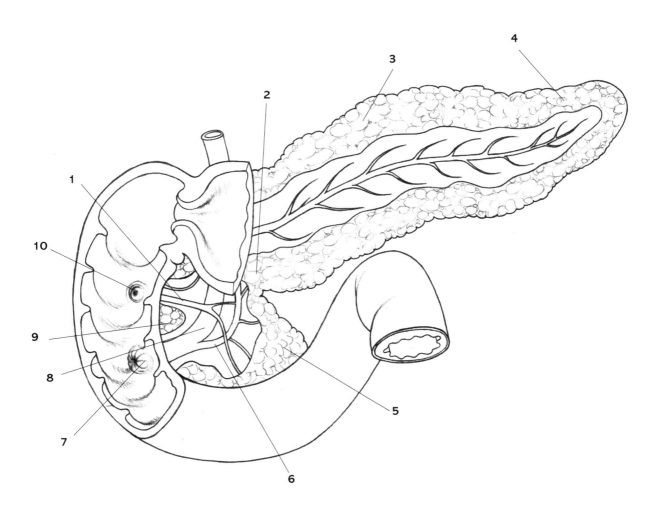

**Key: 1.** accessory pancreatic duct  **2.** neck of pancreas  **3.** body of pancreas  **4.** tail of pancreas  **5.** uncinate
process of pancreas  **6.** main pancreatic duct  **7.** major duodenal papilla  **8.** common bile duct  **9.** head of pancreas
**10.** minor duodenal papilla

# THE JEJUNUM AND ILEUM

The jejunum commences at the duodenojejunal flexure and forms two fifths of the small intestine, where digestion and absorption of food occur. The entire small intestine averages 6m (20ft) in length. The jejunum is wider and more vascular than the ileum and has thicker walls. The ileum, the remaining three fifths of the small intestine, terminates in the right iliac fossa by opening into the caecum via the ileocecal valve. Lymphoid follicles are present in the submucosa of the ileum. The caecum is a dilated blind pouch that is completely covered by peritoneum. Its three taeniae converge on to its posteromedial part, where the appendix is attached by a short mesentery. The position of the appendix is variable.

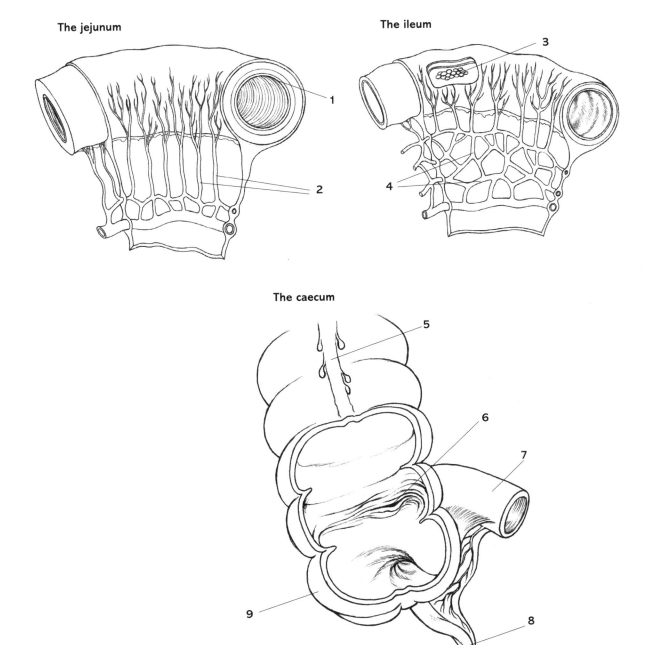

**The jejunum**

**The ileum**

**The caecum**

**Key: 1.** circular folds **2.** long, straight arteries **3.** lymphoid follicles **4.** complex vascular arcades **5.** taenia **6.** opening of ileocaecal valve **7.** terminal ileum **8.** appendix **9.** caecum

## THE COLON

The large intestine extends from the caecum to the anus and is around 2m (6ft) long. It consists of the caecum and appendix, ascending colon, transverse colon, descending colon, sigmoid colon, rectum and anal canal. Peritoneum invests the anterior and lateral surfaces of the ascending and descending colon, while the transverse and sigmoid colon have mesenteries. Features distinguishing the large intestine from the small intestine include taeniae coli (condensations of the longitudinal muscle into three bands), haustra (due to the muscle being shorter than the rest of the wall) and appendices epiploicae (tags of fat projecting from the wall). The main function of the large intestine is the reabsorption of water and electrolytes.

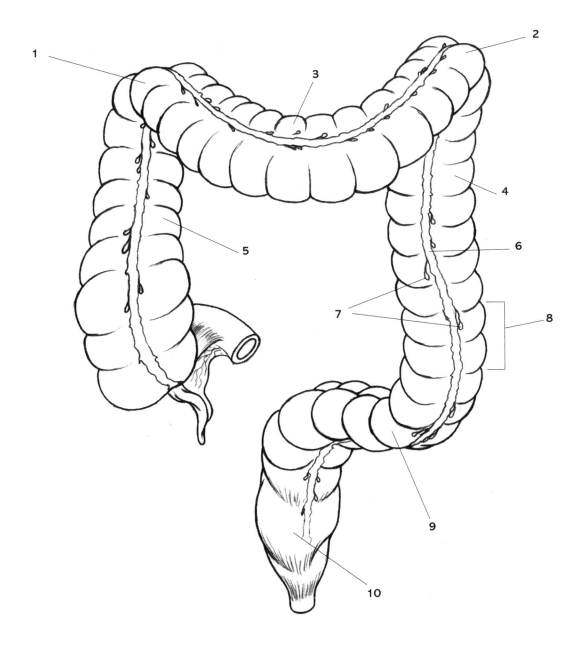

**Key: 1.** hepatic flexure  **2.** splenic flexure  **3.** transverse colon  **4.** descending colon  **5.** ascending colon  **6.** taenia coli  **7.** appendices epiploicae  **8.** haustra  **9.** sigmoid colon  **10.** rectum

## THE RECTUM

The rectum commences anterior to the third sacral vertebra as the continuation of the sigmoid colon. It passes downwards in the concavity of the sacrum and turns anteriorly at the coccyx as the dilated ampulla. After a short course, it bends posteriorly to pass through the pelvic diaphragm and puborectalis sling to become the anal canal, which runs posteroinferiorly to open onto the exterior at the anus. The upper part of the anal canal is endodermal in origin and is covered by colonic mucosa, with up to 10 longitudinal folds (anal columns) arching into the lumen. The lower part is ectodermal and lined by skin. The dentate (white) line represents the junction of skin with mucous membrane.

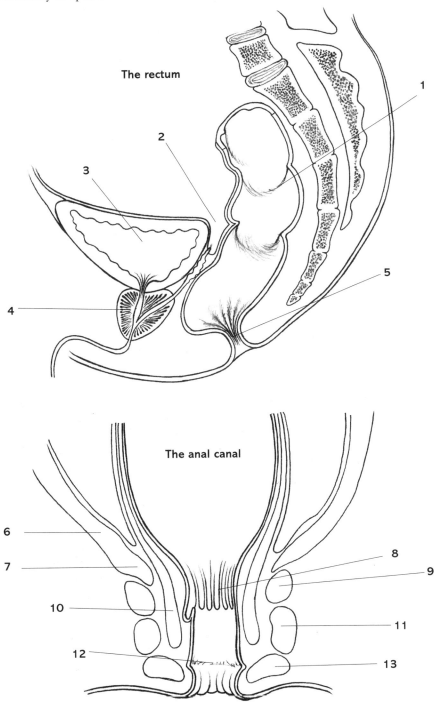

The rectum

The anal canal

Key: 1. rectum  2. rectovesical pouch (in males)  3. bladder  4. prostate gland  5. anal canal

6. levator ani  7. puborectalis  8. anal column  9. deep part of external anal sphincter  10. internal anal sphincter
11. superficial part of external anal sphincter  12. dentate line  13. subcutaneous part of external anal sphincter

# THE URINARY SYSTEM

The urinary system comprises the kidneys, ureters, bladder and urethra. In the male, both urinary and genital organs have a common terminal channel to the exterior. The kidneys lie on the posterior abdominal wall, with their hila at the level of the first lumbar vertebra. The right kidney lies slightly lower than the left because of the liver. On each side, the renal pelvis continues as the ureter. The ureters descend in line with the tips of the transverse processes of the lumbar vertebrae. The three 'natural constrictions' where the ureters are at their narrowest occur at the pelviureteric junction, the pelvic brim and the ureteric orifices.

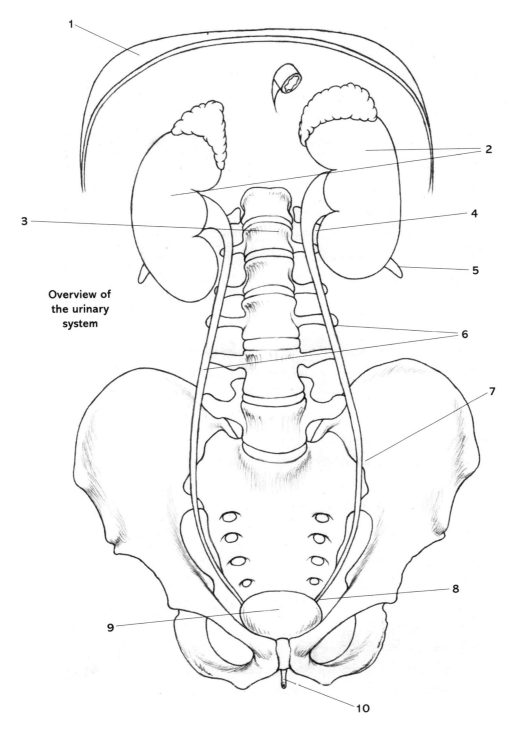

Overview of
the urinary
system

**Key: 1.** diaphragm  **2.** kidneys  **3.** first lumbar vertebra  **4.** 'natural constriction' at the pelviureteric junction
**5.** twelfth rib  **6.** ureters  **7.** 'natural constriction' at the pelvic inlet  **8.** 'natural constriction' at the ureteric orifice
**9.** bladder  **10.** urethra

## THE KIDNEYS

The kidneys are partly covered by peritoneum anteriorly and the relations differ on each side. Posteriorly, they are both related to the diaphragm, the twelfth rib, the quadratus lumborum and psoas major muscles, and the lumbar fascia. At the upper poles are the adrenal glands, which lie outside the renal capsules. In addition to their role in urine production, the kidneys produce hormones and the enzyme renin. Each kidney has a cortex and a medulla. The latter comprises renal pyramids that converge onto calyces extending from the renal pelvis. Each calyx receives a papilla. At each renal hilum are the tributaries of the renal vein, branches of the renal artery and the renal pelvis.

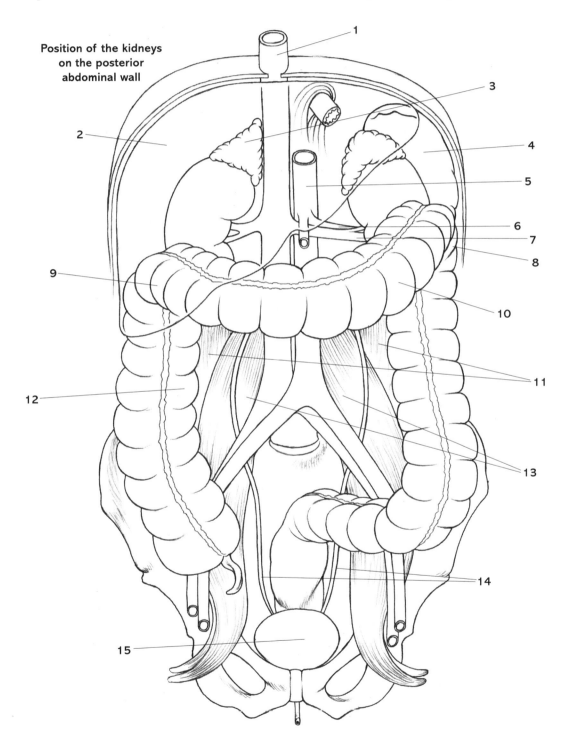

Position of the kidneys on the posterior abdominal wall

**Key: 1.** inferior vena cava  **2.** liver  **3.** adrenals  **4.** spleen  **5.** abdominal aorta  **6.** renal artery  **7.** renal vein
**8.** splenic flexure of colon  **9.** hepatic flexure of colon  **10.** transverse colon  **11.** quadratus lumborum
**12.** ascending colon  **13.** psoas major  **14.** ureters  **15.** bladder

**Internal structure of kidney**

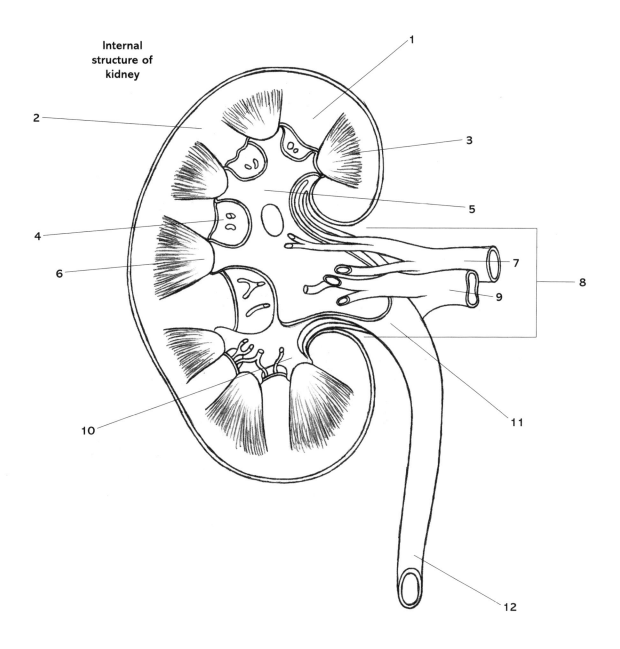

**Key: 1.** renal column  **2.** cortex  **3.** medulla  **4.** renal sinus  **5.** major calyx  **6.** renal papilla  **7.** renal artery  **8.** hilum
**9.** renal vein  **10.** minor calyx  **11.** renal pelvis  **12.** ureter

## THE BLADDER

The urinary bladder lies immediately posterior to the pubic symphysis in the pelvis. Its apex is connected to the umbilicus by the median umbilical ligament (urachus) and the medial umbilical ligaments (obliterated umbilical arteries). Its triangular base (trigone) is adherent to the pelvic floor. The urethral opening is at the anteroinferior end of the trigone, while the ureters enter obliquely at the two posterolateral angles. The ductus deferens passes along the inferolateral surface, medial to the ureter and the medial umbilical ligament. The base of the bladder is separated from the rectum by the rectovesical pouch (males) and by the uterovesical pouch (females). The common ejaculatory ducts open into the floor of the prostatic urethra in the male.

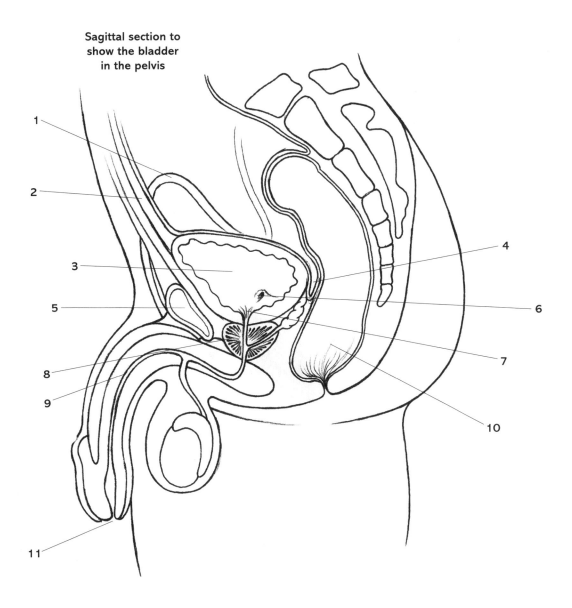

**Sagittal section to show the bladder in the pelvis**

**Key: 1.** ductus deferens **2.** median umbilical ligament **3.** bladder **4.** rectovesical pouch **5.** pubis **6.** ureteric orifice **7.** internal urethral meatus **8.** prostate gland **9.** urethra **10.** rectum **11.** external urethral meatus

**Coronal section
showing internal
features of the bladder**

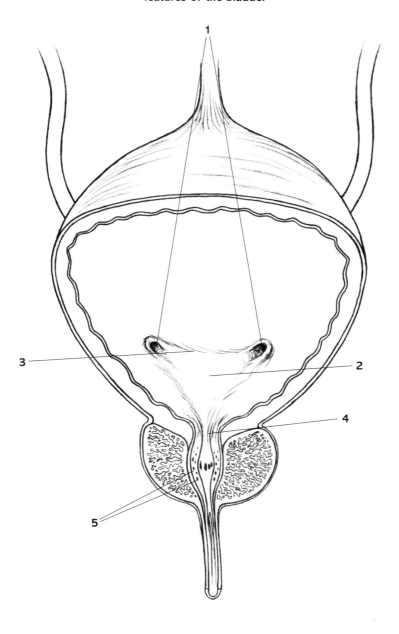

**Key: 1.** ureteric orifices  **2.** trigone  **3.** interureteric bar  **4.** internal urethral meatus  **5.** openings of prostatic ducts

# THE REPRODUCTIVE SYSTEM

## OVERVIEW OF THE FEMALE PELVIC CONTENTS

This sagittal view of the pelvis shows the relationship of the viscera within the female pelvis supported by the pelvic floor. The urethra, vagina and the anal canal are all seen to pierce the pelvic floor. The organs of the urogenital system are anterior, and those of the gastrointestinal system are posterior. The urinary bladder lies in front and beneath the uterus. This relationship changes when the bladder fills or the uterus is in a pregnant state. The ovary sits on the lateral wall of the pelvis with the fallopian tube and its fimbria nearby running in the broad ligament of the uterus to join the uterine body just distal to the fundus.

The rectum is partly covered by peritoneum, particularly in the proximal one third.

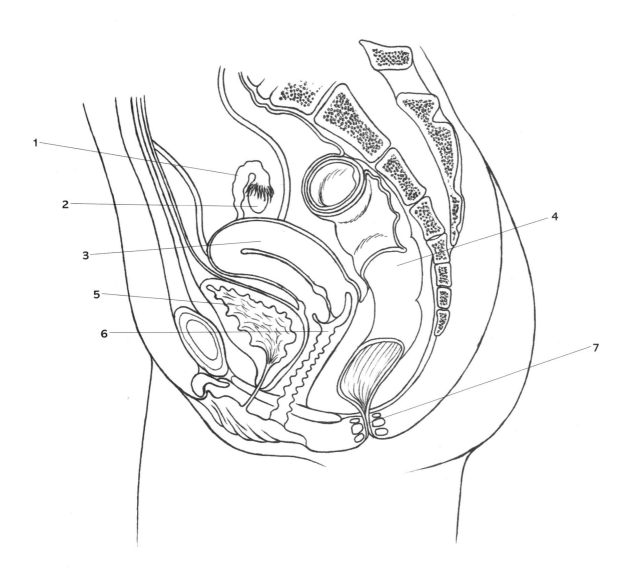

**Key: 1.** uterine tube  **2.** ovary  **3.** uterus  **4.** rectum  **5.** urinary bladder  **6.** vagina  **7.** anal canal

## THE PERINEAL BODY IN THE FEMALE

The perineal body forms the central point of insertion of a number of the muscles that form the floor of the pelvic outlet. These include the superficial transverse perineal muscles laterally, the bulbospongiosus muscles anteriorly and the external anal sphincter posteriorly. Also related to the perineal body are the other muscles of the floor of the pelvis, including the levator ani. In the male, the puborectalis has fibres going to it as it passes posteriorly to surround the rectum. In acting as a central insertion of muscles, the perineal body is an important structure in contributing to the support of the pelvic contents within the pelvis.

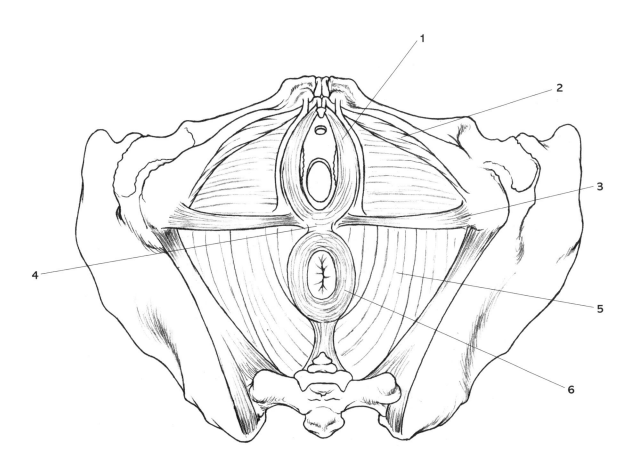

## FEMALE MUSCLES IN SUPERFICIAL PERINEAL POUCH

The muscles in this diagram of the superficial perineal pouch in the female are concerned with control of the pelvic floor, support of the perineum and sphincteric control, together with urethral emptying at the end of micturition. There are slightly different functions depending on whether the subject is male or female.

The bulbospongiosus muscle in the female originates at the perineal body and goes forwards to encircle the vagina and the body of the clitoris. It probably acts as a sphincter of the vaginal orifice. The ischiocavernosus muscle covers the crus of the corpus cavernosum on both sides. It originates on the ischiopubic ramus and inserts into the side of the crus in the male and covers the crus of the clitoris in the female. Its action is to compress the crus.

The superficial transverse perineal muscles support the centre of the perineum, originating on the medial aspect of the ischial tuberosity and inserting into the central tendon of the perineum and perineal body.

The nerve supply of all these muscles is the perineal branch of the pudendal nerve.

**Key: 1.** bulbocavernosus muscle **2.** ischiocavernosus muscle **3.** superficial transverse perineal muscle **4.** perineal body **5.** levator ani **6.** external anal sphincter

## THE GENITO-URINARY TRACT OF THE FEMALE

The genito-urinary tract of the female consists of the ovaries (not seen in this diagram); the uterine tubes, with their proximal openings and fimbria that surround and neighbour the ovary; the uterus, consisting of a fundus, a body and a cervix; and the vaginal canal, which joins the cervix to the exterior in the perineum. The uterus lies within the pelvis between the bladder anteriorly and the rectum posteriorly. The ovaries lie on the side wall of the pelvis, neighbouring the fimbria of the uterine or fallopian tubes. Conception occurs within the fallopian tube, and the conceptus travels into the uterus, where it attaches and develops into an embryo. In normal pregnancies, the baby is born by expulsion from the uterus through a dilated cervix and into the vagina, from where it is delivered to the outside.

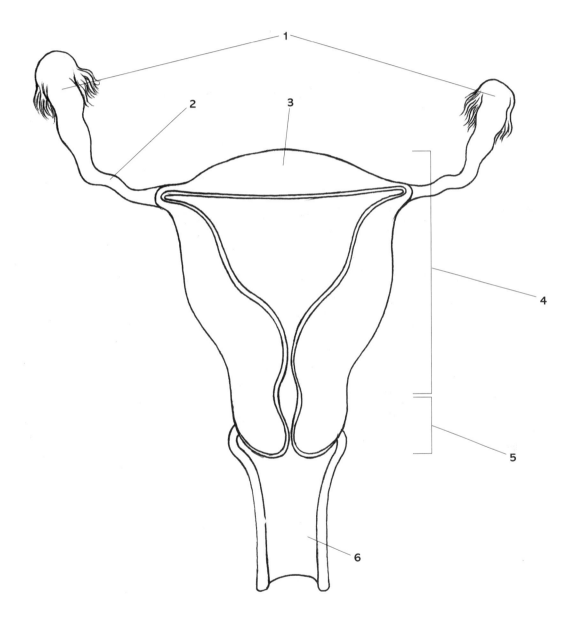

**Key: 1.** opening of uterine tubes **2.** uterine tube **3.** fundus of uterus **4.** body of uterus **5.** cervix of uterus **6.** vagina

## FEMALE PELVIS PERITONEAL FOLDS

As in the male pelvis, the peritoneum descending from the abdomen into the female pelvis reflects to cover the surfaces of the pelvic organs. This saggital view of the pelvic contents shows how the peritoneum comes down on the interior of the anterior abdominal wall, reflects on to the superior surface of the bladder, and then reflects on to the anterior surface of the uterus, forming the vesico-uterine pouch. This pouch is reduced in size as the bladder fills with urine. The peritoneum then covers the body of the uterus and descends on the posterior surface of the uterus to the level of the posterior wall of the vagina, where it reflects again, this time on to the anterior wall of the rectum, forming the rectouterine pouch of Douglas. The fallopian tube and round ligament of the uterus lie within folds of peritoneum on either side of the uterus. The broad ligament of the uterus is made of the lateral extension of the peritoneum that reflects over the uterus. The vagina, lower rectum and bladder are all extraperitoneal, as are the ovaries, the inferior epigastric arteries and the ureters.

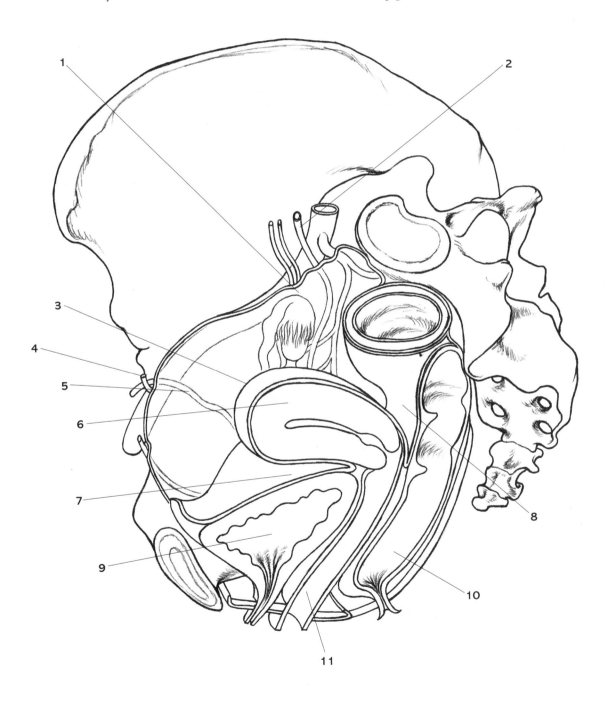

Key: **1.** uterine tube  **2.** ureter  **3.** fundus  **4.** inferior epigastric artery  **5.** round ligament  **6.** uterus  **7.** vesico-uterine pouch  **8.** rectum  **9.** bladder  **10.** rectum  **11.** vagina

## FEMALE EXTERNAL GENITALIA

The female external genitalia consist of the labia majora and minora, the vaginal opening and the clitoris. Anteriorly, the symphysis pubis lies in front of the clitoris; it comprises the two crura and the glans clitoris. The corpora cavernosa form the body of the clitoris. The vaginal opening is bounded externally on either side by the labia majora. Deep to the labia majora are the labia minora, which form the bulb of the vestibule and meet posteriorly to form the vaginal fornix, on either side of which are the greater vestibular glands. Posterior to the clitoris is the urethral opening. The ischial tuberosities on either side give origin to the transverse perineal muscles, which insert into the perineal body that sits behind the posterior fornix of the vagina.

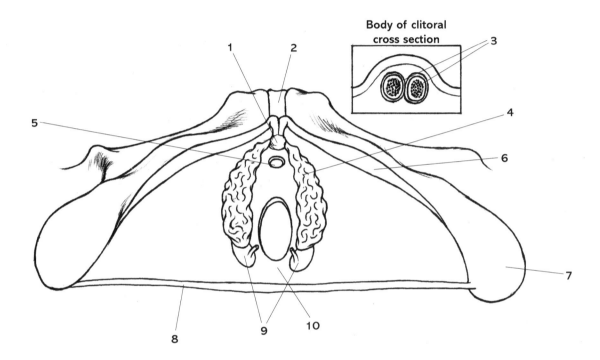

**Key: 1.** glans clitoris  **2.** symphysis pubis  **3.** corpora cavernosa  **4.** bulbo spongiosus muscle  **5.** urethra  **6.** clitoral crus  **7.** ischial tuberosity  **8.** superficial transverse perineal muscle  **9.** vestibular glands  **10.** perineal body

## OVERVIEW OF THE MALE PELVIC CONTENTS

This is a midline sagittal section of the male pelvis. Anteriorly, the abdominal wall is seen to descend towards the pubis, becoming the dorsal surface of the penis, while posteriorly, the vertebral column includes the lower end of the lumbar vertebrae, the sacrum and the coccygeal bones. This is a male pelvis with the obvious male reproductive organs and external genitalia. Within the pelvis are seen the contents that anteriorly include the bladder, the prostate gland lying underneath it, the ejaculatory duct entering the prostatic urethra from the

seminal vesicles, and, more inferiorly, the penis with the contained penile urethra. Inferiorly, outside the pelvis are the testicles, with the vas deferens (the tubular structure going from the testis through the abdominal wall in the inguinal canal, and into the seminal vesicle).

Within the pelvis, posterior to the bladder, is the rectum, which terminates at the anus. Other structures seen in this diagram include the ureter, which is the tube heading from the kidney into the bladder.

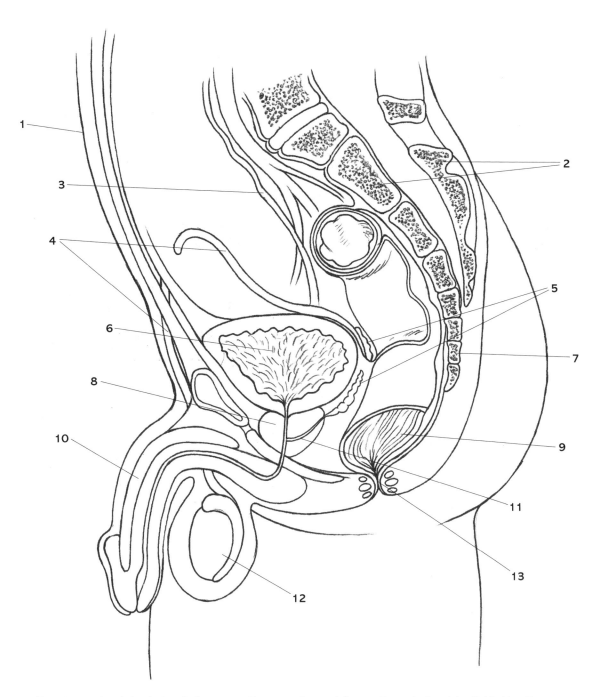

**Key: 1.** anterior abdominal wall **2.** sacrum **3.** ureter **4.** vas deferens **5.** seminal vesicle **6.** bladder **7.** coccyx **8.** prostate **9.** rectum **10.** penis **11.** ejaculatory duct **12.** testes **13.** anus

## MALE PELVIC PERITONEAL FOLDS

The distal end of the peritoneal cavity lies superior and folds into and between the organs within the pelvis. In the male, as seen here, the peritoneum descends the anterior abdominal wall, reflects on to the superior surface of the bladder, and descends into the pouch between the bladder and the rectum (rectovesical pouch). It is reflected to the front and sides of the rectum to varying degrees throughout the length of the rectum. External to the peritoneum anteriorly is the inferior epigastric artery, laterally the common iliac artery, posteriorly the ureter, and laterally the vas deferens. Anterior to the bladder lies the symphysis pubis, with the retropubic space immediately posterior to the symphysis and anterior to the bladder. The bladder is also extraperitoneal in the pelvis.

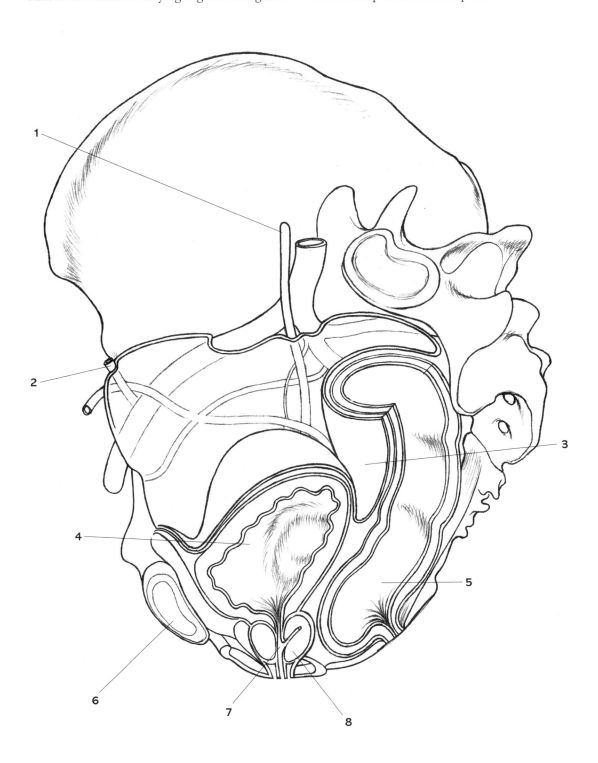

**Key: 1.** ureter  **2.** inferior epigastric artery  **3.** rectovesical pouch  **4.** bladder  **5.** rectum  **6.** symphysis pubis  **7.** prostatic urethra  **8.** prostate

## MALE EXTERNAL GENITALIA

This drawing is of the penis, part of the male external genitalia, the functions of which are to transmit urine from the urinary bladder and semen from the seminal vesicles to the outside. The anatomy of the penis facilitates such functions. The penis consists of three tubelike structures. Two of these tubes are known as corpora cavernosa and contain varying amounts of blood. The third structure, a spongy cylinder called the corpus spongiosum, houses the urethra. The penile urethra is serviced by a pair of bulbourethral glands as it emerges from the perineum; this area is called the bulb of the penis. The corpora cavernosa originate in the crura, and the ischiocavernosus muscles cover the crus on each side.

The terminal end of the urethra is the external urethral meatus; just proximal to this is the navicular fossa of the penile urethra, which is thought to be responsible for keeping the external urethral meatus cleansed by allowing a more turbulent flow of urine as it emerges. The distal end of the penis is bell-shaped and this is the glans penis.

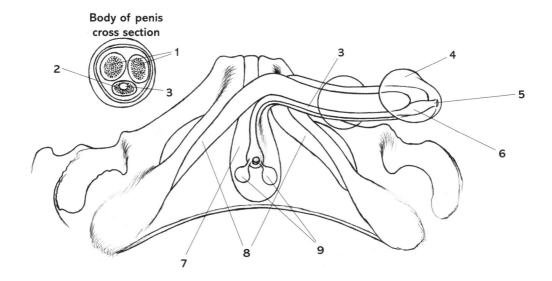

Key: **1.** corpora cavernosa **2.** corpus spongiosum **3.** urethra **4.** glans penis **5.** external urethral orifice
**6.** navicular fossa of urethra **7.** penile bulb **8.** crura of the penis **9.** bulbourethral glands

# OSTEOLOGY

## SKELETON

The exact number of bones in the skeleton varies from human to human. Neonates have at least 270, and sometimes in excess of 300, bones but, by the time they have reached adulthood, this total has been reduced to around 206 by the fusion of adjacent bones, such as the coccyx and the sacrum. Not every bone is interconnected: for example, the three ossicles in the ear are joined only to each other. Female skeletons tend to have narrower rib cages and larger pelves than their male equivalents. In both sexes, the largest bone is the femur and the smallest the stapes in the middle ear. The skeleton is supported by cartilage, ligaments, muscles and tendons.

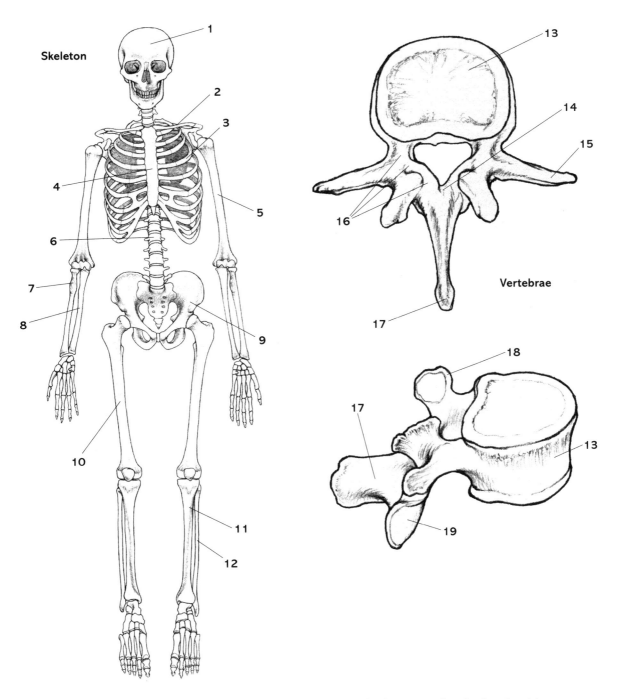

Skeleton

Vertebrae

**Key: 1.** skull  **2.** clavicle  **3.** ribs  **4.** sternum  **5** humerus  **6.** vertebral column  **7.** radius  **8.** ulna  **9.** pelvis  **10.** femur  **11.** tibia  **12.** fibula

**13.** vertebral body  **14.** vertebral arch  **15.** transverse process  **16.** lamina and pedicle  **17.** spinal process  **18.** superior articular process  **19.** inferior articular process

## THE SKULL: LATERAL VIEW

This lateral view of the skull shows the bones that form the vault of the skull as well as the side of the face, including the zygoma, temporal bone, maxilla and mandible. In the region of the orbit, the lacrimal bone is seen to form part of the medial wall, while the nasal bones are between the orbits and anterior to them. The pterion is the point where the frontal, parietal and temporal bones meet at the upper end of the greater wing of the sphenoid. This point overlies the middle meningeal artery. The asterion is the point where the occipital, parietal and mastoid part of the temporal bones meet. The suture lines are the junctions between the various bones that form the skull. In infancy, there is expandability at these sutures, but this is not the case in the adult skull.

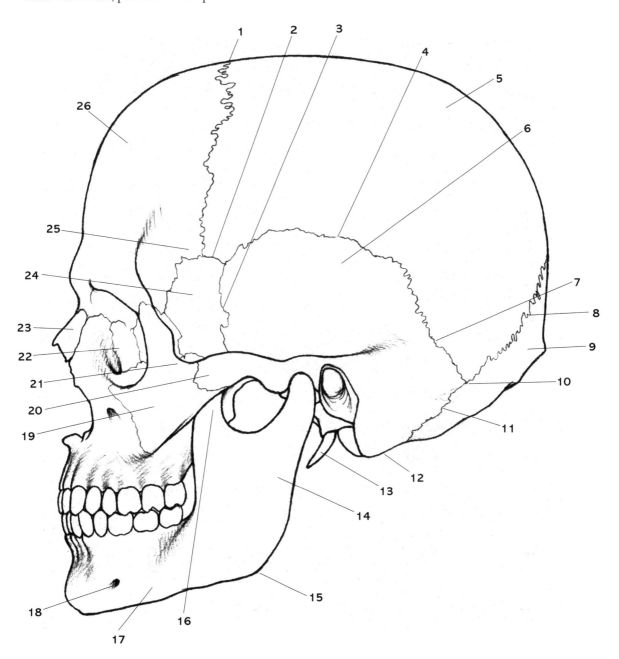

**Key: 1.** coronal suture  **2.** sphenoparietal suture  **3.** spheno-squamous suture  **4.** squamous suture  **5.** parietal bone  **6.** temporal bone  **7.** parietomastoid suture  **8.** lambdoid suture  **9.** occipital bone  **10.** asterion  **11.** occipitomastoid suture  **12.** mastoid process  **13.** styloid process  **14.** ramus of mandible  **15.** angle of mandible  **16.** coronoid process of mandible  **17.** body of mandible  **18.** mental foramen of mandible  **19.** zygoma  **20.** zygomatic process of temporal bone  **21.** temporal process of zygomatic bone  **22.** lacrimal bone  **23.** nasal bone  **24.** greater wing of sphenoid bone  **25.** pterion  **26.** frontal bone

## THE SKULL: POSTERIOR VIEW

The posterior view of the skull is made up of the occipital bone inferiorly and the parietal bones (right and left) superiorly. On the occipital bone, the nuchal lines give rise to muscles that go down to the neck. The mastoid bones on either side contain the mastoid air cells. The spinal cord continues from the base of the brain, emerging from the skull through the foramen magnum at the inferior part of the occiput posteriorly.

## THE SKULL: SUPERIOR ASPECT

The superior surface of the skull is made of up the frontal, parietal and occipital bones, which are joined by sutures. The anterior one third is made up of the frontal bone, with the coronal suture running at its posterior margin between it and the parietal bones. The midpoint of the coronal suture, where the sagittal and coronal sutures meet, is called the bregma. The suture line between the parietal bones and the occipital bone is called the lambdoid suture. The point where this is met by the sagittal suture is called the lambda.

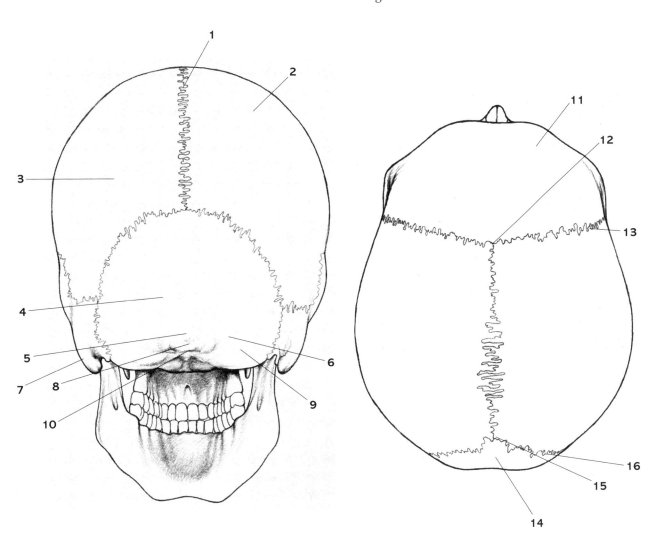

**Key: 1.** sagittal suture  **2.** parietal bone  **3.** parietal bone  **4.** occipital bone  **5.** external occipital protuberance
**6.** superior nuchal line  **7.** mastoid process  **8.** inion  **9.** inferior nuchal line  **10.** external occipital crest

**11.** frontal bone  **12.** bregma  **13.** coronal suture  **14.** occipital bone  **15.** lambda  **16.** lambdoid suture

# THE SKULL: INTERIOR VIEW

The inferior surface of the skull consists of the hard palate anteriorly, made up of the maxillary and palatine bones of the hard palate. Immediately posterior to the hard palate is the posterior nasal aperture that connects the nose to the pharynx, lateral to which are the wings of the sphenoid bone. It is important to note the foramina of the skull and their contents. The foramen lacerum is filled with cartilage in the adult. Posterolateral to the foramen lacerum is the carotid canal, while lateral to it are the foramen ovale and foramen spinosum. The foramen ovale allows structures to pass between the infratemporal fossa and the middle cranial fossa. These include the mandibular and lesser petrosal nerves. The stylomastoid foramen transmits the facial nerve, while the internal jugular vein emerges through the jugular foramen. The large foramen magnum is the site of the beginning of the spinal cord.

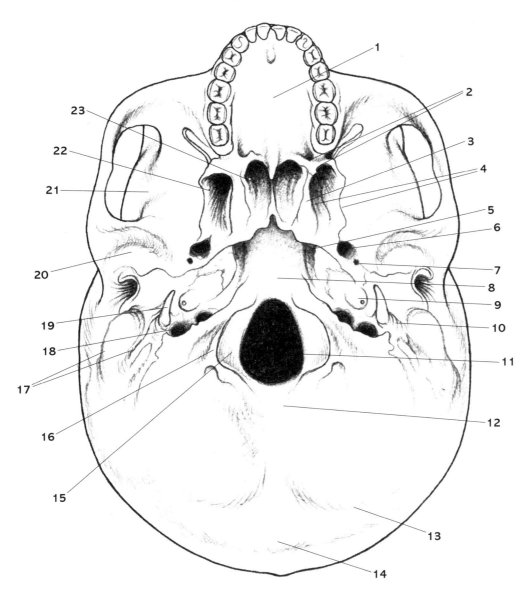

**Key: 1.** hard palate  **2.** greater and lesser palatine foramina  **3.** sphenoid body  **4.** lateral plate of pterygoid process and medial plate of pterygoid process  **5.** foramen lacerum  **6.** foramen ovale  **7.** foramen spinosum  **8.** basilar part of the occipital bone  **9.** carotid canal  **10.** stylomastoid foramen  **11.** foramen magnum  **12.** external occipital crest  **13.** inferior and superior nuchal lines  **14.** external occipital protuberance  **15.** occipital condyle  **16.** hypoglossal canal  **17.** mastoid process and mastoid notch  **18.** jugular foramen  **19.** styloid process  **20.** mandibular fossa  **21.** greater wing of sphenoid bone  **22.** pterygoid fossa  **23.** posterior nasal aperture

# THE UPPER MUSCULOSKELETAL SYSTEM

This overview of the skeleton shows the skull atop the spinal column, at the distal end of which is the pelvis. In the thoracic area is the rib cage, with the upper limbs attached to the spinal column and thorax through the clavicles and the scapulae. The lower limbs are attached to the pelvis through the hip joints. Structures towards the midline are described as medial; those away from the midline are described as lateral. Some bones are paired, and others are unpaired. The ribs, the clavicle, the sides of the pelvis and the scapulae are paired. The bones of the spinal column are all unpaired.

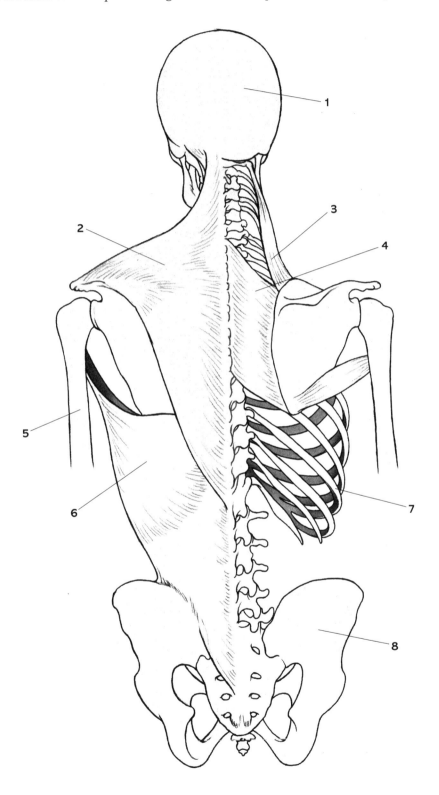

**Key: 1.** skull  **2.** trapezius  **3.** levator scapular  **4.** rhomboids major and rhomboids minor  **5.** humerus
**6.** latissimus dorsi  **7.** ribs  **8.** pelvis

## RIGHT ACROMIOCLAVICULAR JOINT

The acromioclavicular joint is situated between the outer end of the clavicle and the acromion. It is a small joint with a disc within it. It is important in maintaining the stability of the scapula on the chest and the distance of the shoulder from the more medial structures. Transverse ligaments go from the clavicle to the acromion anteriorly, superiorly, inferiorly and posteriorly and control some of the movements and stability of the joint. Vertical forces on the clavicle, however, tend to make it rise superiorly, and this movement is stabilised by the inferiorly directed coracoclavicular ligament, which has two parts, trapezoid and conoid. The conoid and trapezoid ligaments are inserted towards the base of the coracoid process of the scapula and the distal part of the clavicle. The clavicle itself is prone to injury and fracture, and while the majority of clavicular fractures are not associated with significant sequelae, an important injury associated with clavicular fractures is a tear of the subclavian vein or artery and an associated brachial plexus injury.

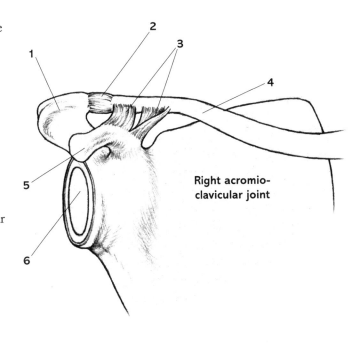

Right acromio-clavicular joint

## MUSCLES OF THE PECTORALIS MAJOR AND DELTOID

The large muscles of the shoulder are the pectoralis major and the deltoid anteriorly and anterolaterally, with posterior elements of the deltoid as well. The deltoid is the muscle on the outer aspect that forms the bulk of the rounded contour of the shoulder, beginning at the acromion, clavicle and scapular spine and inserting into the deltoid tubercle of the humerus on the lateral aspect of the humeral shaft. Supplied by the axillary nerve, it is an abductor and a rotator, flexor, and extensor of the humerus in the shoulder. The anterior aspect of the chest wall is made up of the pectoralis major. Parts of this muscle converge to form a tendon that inserts into the lateral border of the bicipital groove overlying the long head of the biceps as it runs through the groove. Between deltoid and pectoralis muscles is the cephalic vein. Proximally, distal to the clavicle, the interval between deltoid, pectoralis major and clavicle forms the infraclavicular triangle, in which is the clavipectoral fascia and through which the cephalic vein pierces deeply to enter the subclavian vein.

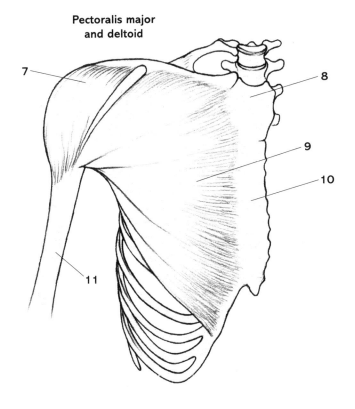

Pectoralis major and deltoid

**Key: 1.** Acromion  **2.** acromio-clavicular ligament  **3.** coraco-clavicular ligament  **4.** clavicle  **5.** coracoid  **6.** glenoid

**7.** deltoid  **8.** manubrium  **9.** pectoralis major  **10.** sternum  **11.** humerus

## MUSCLES OF THE ARM AND AXILLA

The pectoralis minor muscle begins by multiple origins from the anterior aspect of the ribs and inserts into the coracoid process of the scapula. It is a scapular stabiliser. In the drawing, the main part of the muscle has been removed and the axillary artery and surrounding nerves of the brachial plexus are seen to lie deep to it. The long head of the biceps is seen to emerge over the top of the humeral head, under the transverse intertubercular ligament, and to head down towards the arm. The short head of the biceps begins on the tip of the coracoid process, and the two heads of the biceps join together to form the main bulk of the biceps muscle on the anterior aspect of the arm. The biceps then runs in front of the elbow to insert into the radius. The various nerves of the brachial plexus are seen, including the median nerve and the ulnar nerve (the radial nerve is not seen). Their origin is in the brachial plexus that surrounds the axillary artery. The ulnar nerve runs medial and posterior to the elbow, behind the medial epicondyle of the humerus.

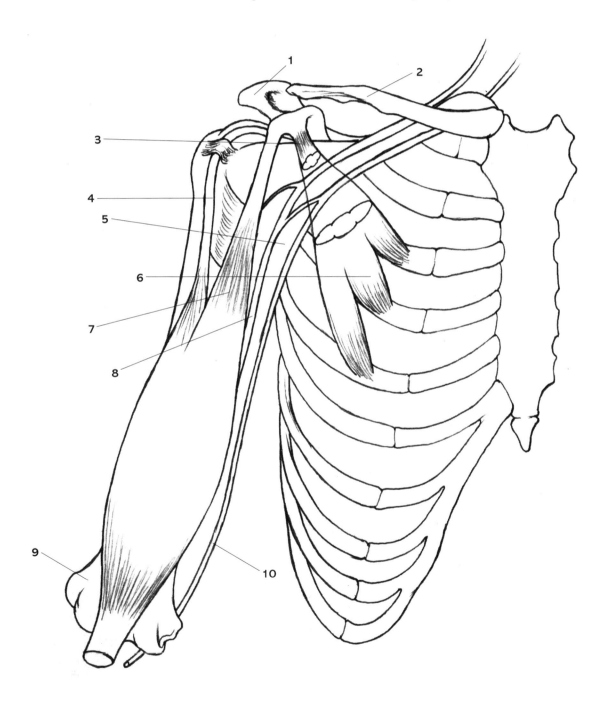

**Key: 1.** acromion  **2.** clavicle  **3.** pectoralis minor proximal cut end  **4.** biceps long head  **5.** axillary artery
**6.** pectoralis minor distal cut end  **7.** biceps short head  **8.** median nerve  **9.** humerus  **10.** ulnar nerve

## BICEPS AND BRACHIALIS MUSCLES

The biceps and brachialis muscles form the bulk of muscle on the anterior aspect of the arm between the shoulder and the elbow. The biceps muscle has two origins. The long head of the biceps begins on the supraglenoid tubercle of the glenoid; the tendon emerges through the intertubercular groove and forms into the muscle bulk on the arm. The short head begins on the coracoid process. In this illustration, the main muscle bulk on the anterior aspect of the arm has been removed to demonstrate the underlying brachialis muscle that begins on the anterior aspect of the humerus. The smaller coracobrachialis muscle begins on the coracoid process and inserts on the medial aspect of the humerus. The biceps muscle inserts into the bicipital tubercle of the radius, seen here with the forearm in supination and the radial tubercle sitting more anteriorly. The brachialis muscle inserts into the coronoid process of the ulna. The brachialis muscle is a prime flexor of the elbow, while the biceps muscle flexes the elbow once the forearm is supinated, it being a strong primary supinator of the forearm. The coracobrachialis is a weak adductor of the shoulder. The long head of the biceps has a stabilising effect on the glenohumeral joint between the humeral head and the scapula.

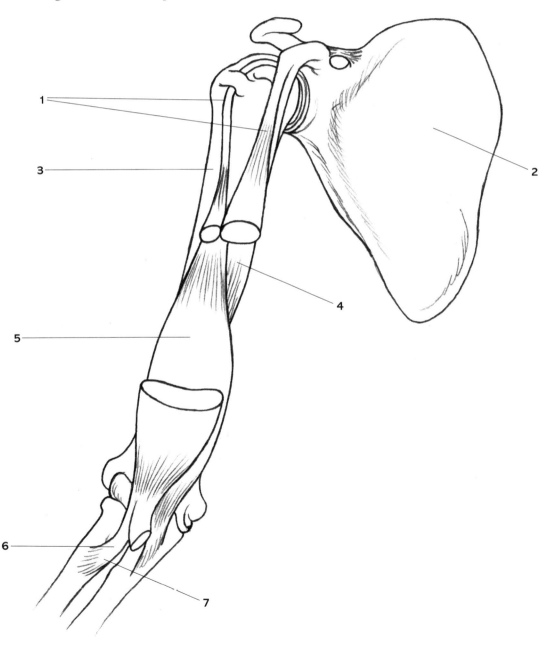

**Key: 1.** short and long heads of biceps  **2.** scapula  **3.** humerus  **4.** coraco-brachialis  **5.** brachialis  **6.** distal tendon of biceps  **7.** radial tubercle

## POSTERIOR MUSCULATURE OF THE SHOULDER AND ARM

This posterior view shows muscles extending from scapula to humerus and across the shoulder joint. Muscles that extend from scapula to humerus affect the glenohumeral joint. Those running superiorly and posteriorly from medial to lateral rotate the humerus by pulling behind or in front of the rotating axis of the shoulder. Above the scapular spine, the supraspinatus inserts laterally into the greater tuberosity of the humerus running superior to the spine of the scapula and under the acromial arch. Distal or inferior to the scapular spine is the infraspinatus, which extends laterally to the greater tuberosity of the humerus in its posterior position. Inferior to that is the teres minor, running to the inferior aspect of the greater tuberosity of the humerus, while the teres major goes laterally into the anteromedial aspect of the humeral shaft.

Supraspinatus assists in abduction of the humerus; infraspinatus and teres minor aid external or lateral rotation of the shoulder; teres major is an internal rotator of the shoulder. With the subscapularis, these muscles form the rotator cuff of the shoulder. Superiorly, the acromion articulates with the end of the clavicle, and the deltoid muscle originates off the acromial spine, the acromion and the clavicle.

The triceps extends from shoulder to elbow on the posterior aspect of the arm. It has three heads. The long head begins on the infraglenoid tubercle and is deep to the teres minor and infraspinatus. The deep medial head originates from the posterior aspect of the humerus. The lateral head originates from the lateral aspect and proximal part of the humerus. The three heads join to form the tendon of the triceps, which inserts into the olecranon process of the ulna.

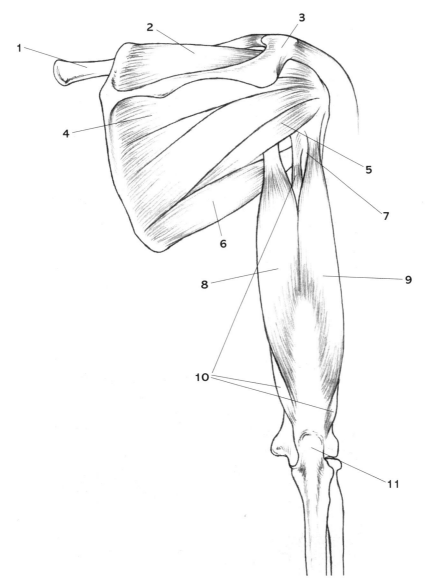

Key: **1.** clavicle  **2.** supraspinatus  **3.** acromion  **4.** infraspinatus  **5.** teres minor  **6.** teres major  **7.** humerus
**8.** triceps long head  **9.** triceps lateral head  **10.** triceps medial head  **11.** olecranon process of ulna

## Elbow joint

The bones of the elbow joint are the humerus, the ulna and the radius. The articular surfaces of the humerus include the capitulum on the radial side and the trochlea on the ulnar side. The radial head and the trochlear notch of the ulna form the distal articular surfaces. The proximal radioulnar joint articulates between the radial head and the radial notch of the ulna. In the proximal shaft of the radius is the radial tuberosity, which here appears anteriorly because the radius is fully supinated. In the pronated position, the radial tuberosity is posterior. Proximal to the trochlea and capitulum is the coronoid fossa, a socket into which the coronoid process of the ulna will enter during full flexion. Flexion of the elbow is carried out by muscles that run anteriorly to the elbow itself and its axis of movement. Extension of the elbow joint is carried out by muscles that run posterior to this axis.

## Contents of the cubital fossa

The cubital fossa is the space on the anterior aspect of the elbow. Its margins are made up of an imaginary line between the epicondyles of the humerus, the pronator teres on the medial side and the brachioradialis on the lateral side. It is a triangular space with the line between the epicondyles situated proximally.

The floor of the antecubital fossa is formed by the brachialis muscle. On the surface in the region of the antecubital fossa are the superficial veins going from distal to proximal. These include the median cubital vein. The cephalic and basilic veins are also seen. Within the cubital fossa are the division of the brachial artery into radial and ulnar arteries, the radial nerve and its deep branch, the superficial branch of the radial nerve and the median nerve.

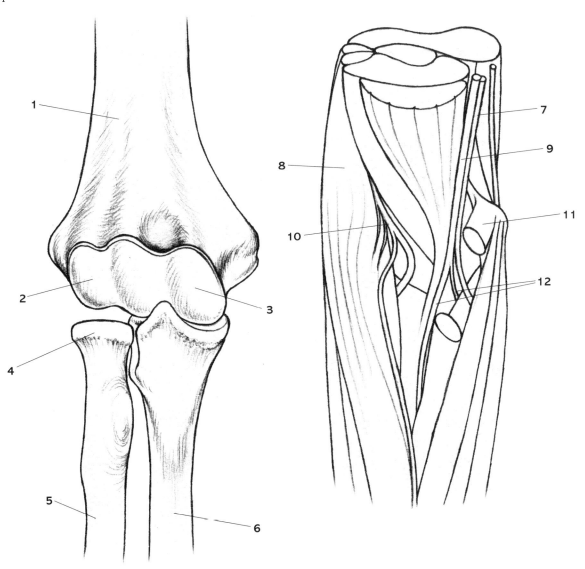

**Key: 1.** humerus  **2.** capitulum  **3.** trochlea  **4.** radial head  **5.** radius  **6.** ulna

**7.** median nerve  **8.** brachioradialis  **9.** brachial artery  **10.** radial nerve  **11.** pronator teres  **12.** radial and ulnar artery

## SUPERFICIAL LAYER OF FOREARM MUSCLES

These muscles comprise the superficial bundle of muscles on the anterior aspect of the forearm and all originate as the common flexor origin on the medial epicondyle, condyle and supracondylar ridge of the humerus. They fan out from their origin and, from the radial to the ulnar side, comprise the pronator teres, the flexor carpi radialis, the palmaris longus (when it exists) and the flexor carpi ulnaris. With the exception of the flexor carpi ulnaris, which is supplied by the ulnar nerve, these muscles are supplied by the median nerve. The flexor carpi ulnaris has two origins, one from the medial epicondyle (common flexor origin) and the other from the medial aspect of the coronoid process of the ulna. Running between the two heads is the ulnar nerve, as it emerges from the tunnel behind the medial epicondyle of the humerus. The pronator teres is the more powerful of the two forearm pronators inserting into the maximum convex point of the radius. The flexor carpi radialis flexes the wrist in conjunction with the flexor carpi ulnaris. While acting on its own it radially deviates and flexes the wrist. The flexor carpi ulnaris acting on its own flexes the wrist into ulnar deviation. The palmaris longus is a vestigial muscle with a short muscle and a long tendon. It inserts into the palmar aponeurosis in the hand. It weakly flexes the wrist in conjunction with other flexors.

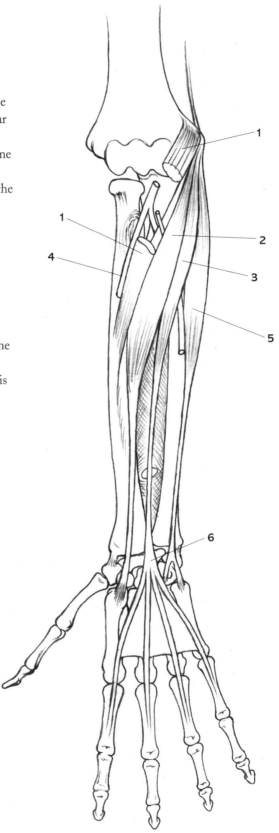

**Key: 1.** pronator teres  **2.** flexor carpi radialis  **3.** palmaris longus  **4.** median nerve  **5.** flexor carpi ulnaris
**6.** palmar aponeurosis

## INTERMEDIATE LAYER OF FOREARM MUSCLES

The flexor digitorum superficialis is a large bulk of muscle on the anterior aspect of the forearm. It is supplied by the median nerve. The tendons insert into the anterior aspect of the base of the middle phalanges of the fingers, splitting into a medial and lateral part anterior to the proximal phalanx to allow the tendons of flexor digitorum profundus to run more distally. In the region of the carpal tunnel the median nerve runs between the tendons of the flexor digitorum superficialis deep to the flexor retinaculum. The ulnar nerve and artery lie medial and are in a separate compartment at the wrist.

## DEEP LAYER OF ANTERIOR FOREARM

The deep muscles on the anterior compartment of the forearm are flexor digitorum profundus, flexor pollicis longus and pronator quadratus. Flexor digitorum profundus contains four tendons extending to the distal phalanges of the fingers; it flexes all the joints that it crosses, including the wrist. Flexor pollicis longus is on the radial side of the forearm; its tendon goes to the distal phalanx of the thumb, crossing deep to the flexor retinaculum within the carpal tunnel. Pronator quadratus runs transversely between radius and ulna and is a weak pronator of the forearm.

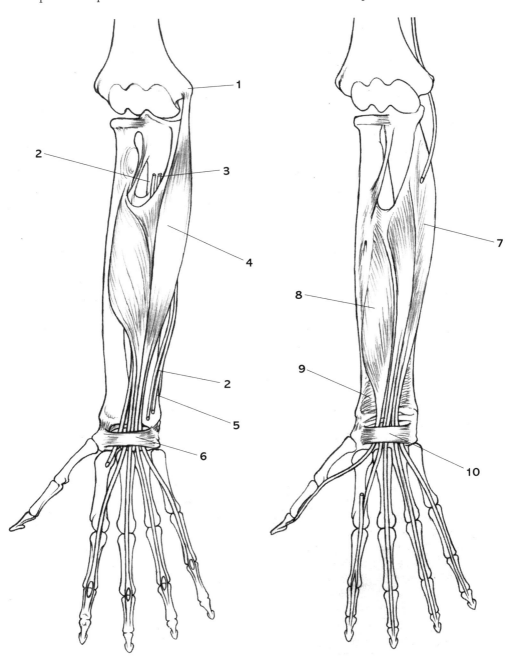

**Key: 1.** medial epicondyle of humerus  **2.** ulnar artery  **3.** median nerve  **4.** flexor digitorum superficialis
**5.** ulnar nerve  **6.** flexor retinaculum

**7.** flexor digitorum profundus  **8.** flexor pollicis longus  **9.** pronator quadratus  **10.** flexor retinaculum

## FOREARM POSTERIOR MUSCLE COMPARTMENT, ANTERIOR VIEW

In this view, we see the brachioradialis muscle, which begins on the lateral aspect of the distal shaft of the humerus in the area of the supracondylar ridge, travels down the lateral aspect of the forearm, and inserts into the styloid process of the radius. The only joint that it crosses is the elbow joint. Although classified in the extensor group of the posterior forearm muscles, in the fully pronated position of the forearm the brachioradialis muscle is a mild elbow flexor.

## FOREARM SUPERFICIAL MUSCLES POSTERIOR COMPARTMENT, POSTERIOR VIEW

These muscles are supplied by the radial nerve and all except the anconeus run through compartments under the extensor retinaculum at the back of the wrist. The first compartment contains the abductor longus and extensor brevis of the thumb; the second, the extensor carpi radialis longus and brevis; the third, the abductor pollicis longus; the fourth, the extensor digitorum communis and indicis; the fifth, the extensor digiti minimi; the sixth, the extensor carpi ulnaris.

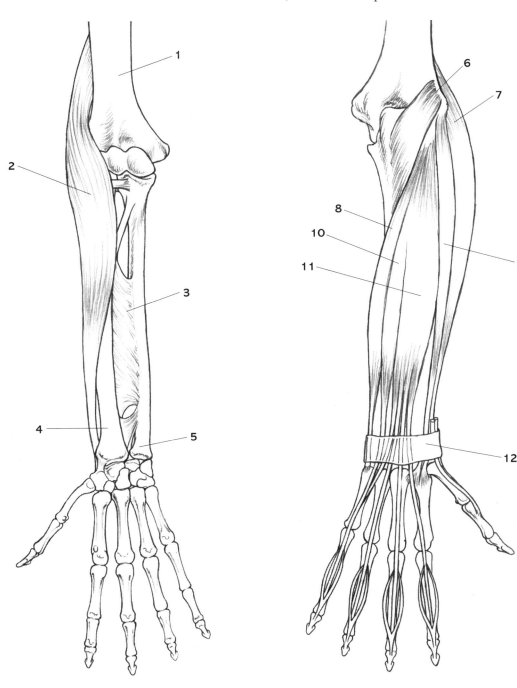

**Key: 1.** hamelus  **2.** brachioradialis  **3.** interosseus membrane  **4.** radius  **5.** ulna

**6.** anconeus  **7.** extensor carpi radialis longus  **8.** extensor carpi ulnaris  **9.** extensor carpi radialis brevis
**10.** extensor digiti minimi  **11.** extensor digitorum  **12.** extensor retinaculum

## THE DEEP MUSCLES OF THE POSTERIOR COMPARTMENT OF THE FOREARM

The deep muscles on the posterior aspect of the forearm are the supinator muscle and the extensors of the thumb, the extensor indicis to the index finger, and the long abductor of the thumb. Most of them originate from the ulna and interosseus membrane, except the superficial head of the supinator and extensor pollicis brevis. They insert into the radial side of the forearm and hand and are all supplied by the radial nerve or its branch, the posterior interosseus nerve. All except the supinator cross the wrist joint and so have an extensor action on the wrist, although their primary function is actually not on the wrist itself.

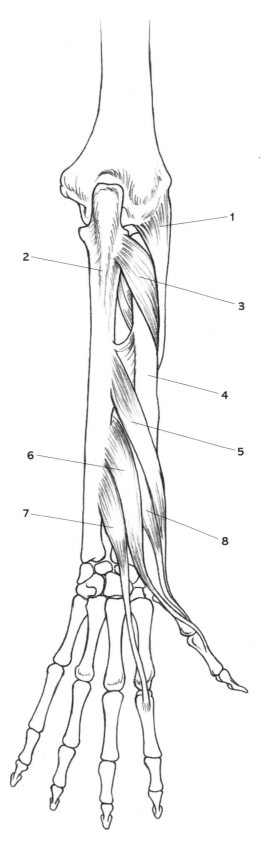

Key: **1.** supinator superficial head  **2.** ulna  **3.** supinator deep head  **4.** radius  **5.** abductor pollicis longus  **6.** extensor pollicis longus  **7.** extensor indicis  **8.** extensor pollicis brevis

# THE LUMBRICAL MUSCLES OF THE HAND

The lumbricals are a group of small muscles that originate from the tendons of the deep flexors of the fingers (flexor digitorum profundus). Generally they originate on the radial side of the tendon and proceed on the radial side of the MCP joint, inserting into the radial aspect of the extensor expansion of the fingers. Thus their action is to flex the metacarpophalangeal joints and extend the proximal interphalangeal joints of the fingers that they serve. There are usually four lumbrical muscles, but as can be seen in the drawing, their origins can be from both the radial and ulnar aspects of the deep flexor tendons. This is variable. The radial two lumbricals are supplied by the median nerve, while the ulnar two lumbricals are supplied by the ulnar nerve. When working together, they put the hand in what is known as the 'writing position' or functional position of the hand, with MCP joint flexion and PIP joint extension. The origin of the lumbrical muscles is distal to the flexor retinaculum. There is no lumbrical muscle originating from the tendon of flexor pollicis longus.

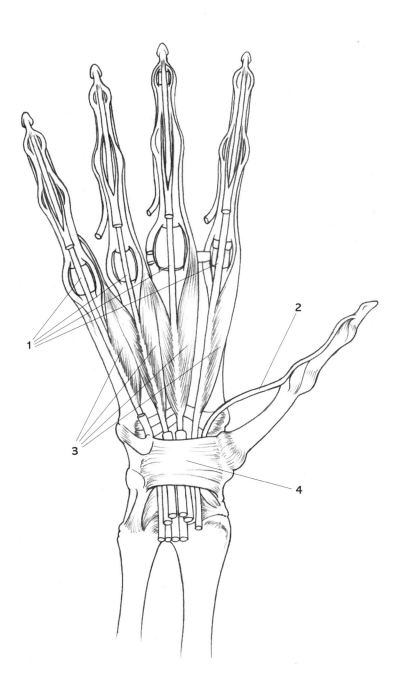

**Key: 1.** flexor digitorum profundus **2.** flexor pollicis longus tendon **3.** lumbricals **4.** flexor retinaculum

# THE LOWER MUSCULOSKELETAL SYSTEM

## PELVIS

The pelvis consists of two lateral sets of bones and a central posterior sacrum. The bones of the pelvis form a ring at the proximal or uppermost end, known as the pelvic inlet. Beginning posteriorly, the sacrum is joined by the sacroiliac joint on either side to the right and left ilium. The wing of the ilium is the large, flat portion on the lateral aspect, with the iliac crest as its uppermost rim. Anteriorly, the iliac crest terminates at the anterior superior iliac spine and posteriorly at the sacroiliac joint. The ilium becomes the pubis anteriorly, and the two pubic bones join together to form the pubic symphysis, with the pubic tubercle lying superiorly and laterally. The ischium is the most inferior and somewhat more posteriorly placed bone, with the large ischial tuberosity on which we sit. The sacrotuberous and sacrospinous ligaments link the sacrum with the ischial spine and the posterior inferior iliac spine respectively. The sacroiliac joint is an extremely strong joint, joining either side of the pelvis and the attached lower limbs through the hip, to the lower end of the vertebral column. Lying in the hollow of the ilium, superior to the pelvic inlet, are abdominal contents. Within the pelvis, the pelvic contents will be seen later in an alternative diagram.

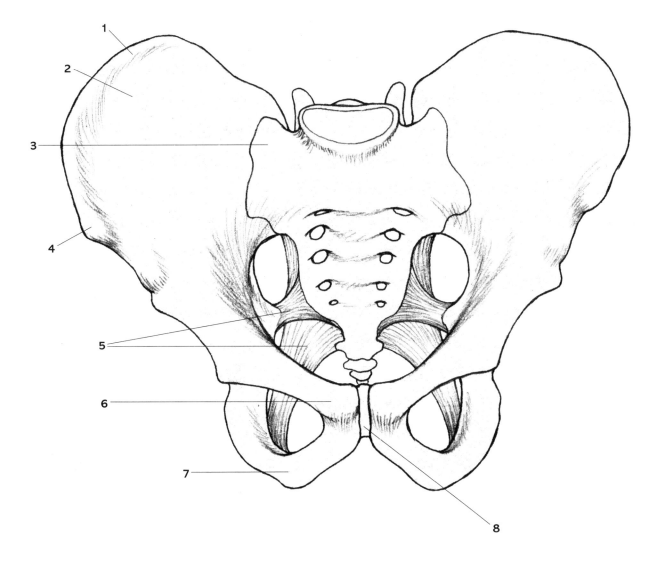

**Key: 1.** iliac crest **2.** ilium **3.** sacroiliac joint **4.** anterior superior iliac spine **5.** sacrotuberous and sacrospinus ligaments **6.** pubic tubercle **7.** ischial tuberosity **8.** symphysis pubis

## ACETABULUM

The acetabulum consists of three parts made up by the ilium, the pubis and the ischium. The acetabulum is the socket of the hip joint in which the head of the femur is located. The ilium forms the wing of the pelvis and the lower lateral aspect of the abdominal cavity wall. The pubic bone is placed anteriorly, and the two pubic bones join together anteriorly to form the symphysis pubis. The ischium has a large tuberosity upon which one sits. The iliac crest (not seen here) is the uppermost margin of the ilium and forms the rim of bone that can be felt at the waist on either side. Structures from within the pelvis emerge through the sacroiliac notch, the obturator foramen and the outlet of the pelvis.

## FEMUR ANTERIOR ASPECT

The femur is the largest long bone in the body and forms part of the hip joint, the knee joint and the thigh bone in between. The proximal aspect of the femur consists of the femoral head, femoral neck, greater and lesser trochanters, subtrochanteric region and femoral shaft. The femoral head forms the ball of the ball-and-socket hip joint, while the femoral neck allows the femoral shaft to be offset from the femoral head and acetabulum. The greater trochanter lies on the proximal aspect of the shaft of the femur laterally, with anterior and posterior aspects, and gives rise to the attachments of the abductors of the thigh (the glutei). The lesser trochanter, which is placed posteriorly but for effect in this drawing has been placed to appear slightly more anteriorly than normal, gives rise to the insertion of the iliacus and psoas muscles, important flexors of the hip.

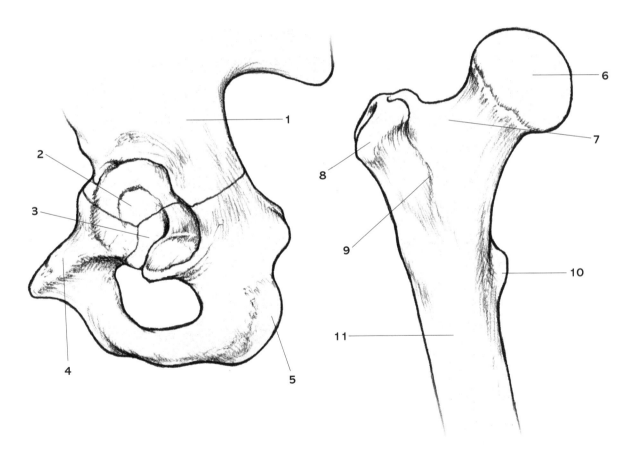

**Key: 1.** ilium  **2.** acetabular fossa  **3.** acetabulum notch  **4.** pubis  **5.** ischium

**6.** head  **7.** neck  **8.** greater trochanter  **9.** inter-trochanteric line  **10.** lesser trochanter  **11.** shaft

## LIGAMENTS OF THE HIP JOINT

This is the left hip seen from the front. The pelvis houses the acetabulum or socket of the hip joint. The ball of the joint is the head of the femur. It is a synovial joint with a capsule and surrounding ligaments that give it stability. Stability is also achieved by the depth of cover of the femoral head within the acetabulum. The three ligaments run across the joint in a spiral fashion to allow the tension to remain constant as the joint moves into different positions. The prominent antero-inferior iliac spine gives rise to muscles, as well as to the ligaments seen in the diagram.

## HIP FLEXORS

The two muscles that make up the powerful hip flexors are the psoas muscle and the iliacus muscle. Both muscles run in front of the axis of flexion of the hip joint and cross it from proximal to distal. The psoas muscle originates in the lumbar spine; it is a strap muscle and is cylindrical in shape. It adjoins with the iliacus muscle, which begins on the inner aspect of the wing of the ilium, to cross deep to the inguinal ligament and insert into the lesser trochanter of the femur. Lying in front of the iliacus muscles are the contents of the abdominal cavity. The inguinal ligament formed by the rolled-up edge of the external oblique muscle runs from the anterior superior iliac spine to the pubic tubercle and forms the proximal border of the femoral triangle.

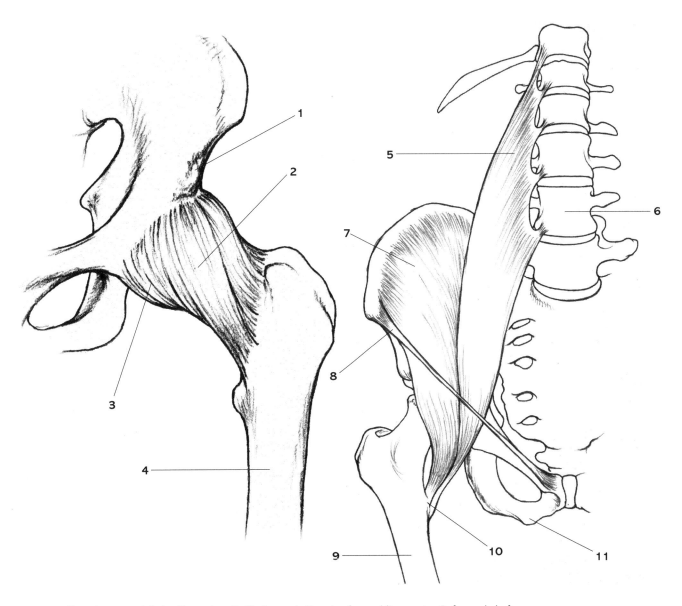

**Key: 1.** antero-inferior iliac spine  **2.** ilio-femoral  **3.** pubo-femoral ligaments  **4.** femoral shaft

**5.** psoas  **6.** vertebral column  **7.** iliacus  **8.** inguinal ligament  **9.** femur  **10.** lesser trochanter  **11.** iscial tuberosities

## FEMORAL TRIANGLE AND SUBSARTORIAL CANAL

The femoral triangle is a triangle on the anterior aspect of the proximal thigh, bounded superiorly by the inguinal ligament, medially by the medial border of the adductor longus muscle, and laterally by the medial border of the sartorius. Its floor consists of the adductor muscles of the thigh and the ilio-psoas muscle more proximally. Its contents include the femoral vein, artery and nerve, going from medial to lateral. The femoral nerve has already begun to divide by the time it enters the triangle. At the apex of the triangle, the femoral vein and femoral artery run into the subsartorial canal under the sartorius muscle, along with the nerve to vastus medialis and the saphenous nerve. Farther distally, the sartorius and gracilis muscles traverse the medial aspect of the knee to insert into the proximal tibia, while the femoral artery descends and runs through the adductor hiatus of the adductor magnus muscle. Within the femoral triangle, the profunda femoris artery arises postero-laterally from the common femoral artery and runs deeply to supply the muscles of the thigh. The long saphenous vein enters anteriorly into the femoral vein within the femoral triangle, through the cribriform fascia, in the region of the saphenous opening. Multiple lymph glands are frequently found in the triangle.

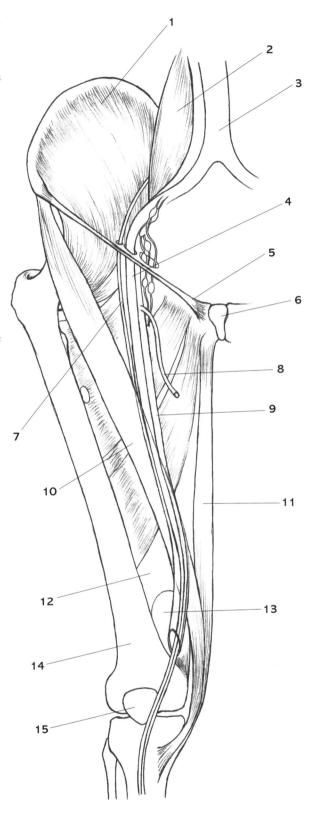

**Key: 1.** iliacus muscle **2.** psoas muscle **3.** aorta **4.** femoral artery **5.** inguinal ligament **6.** symphysis pubis **7.** femoral nerve **8.** long saphenous vein **9.** femoral vein **10.** sartorius **11.** gracilis **12.** adductor magnus **13.** adductor hiatus **14.** femur **15.** patella

# GLUTEAL REGION SUPERFICIAL (MUSCLES)

Examining the muscles of the gluteal region, one is faced with the gluteus maximus, medius and minimus. On reflecting, the gluteus maximus and gluteus medius the minimus are visible. Farther distally, the short external rotators of the femur come into view, beginning with the piriformis, the obturator internus with the superior and inferior gamellus above and below it. Most distal of all is the quadratus femoris, a rectangular-shaped muscle inserting into the posterior aspect of the proximal femur. The gluteus maximus (not seen in this diagram) is the large muscle that gives the rounded shape to the buttock. It is an abductor and rotator of the hip joint. Gluteus medius internally rotates the hip, as does gluteus minimus. Gluteus maximus is supplied by the inferior gluteal nerve, but gluteus medius and minimus are both supplied by the superior gluteal nerve.

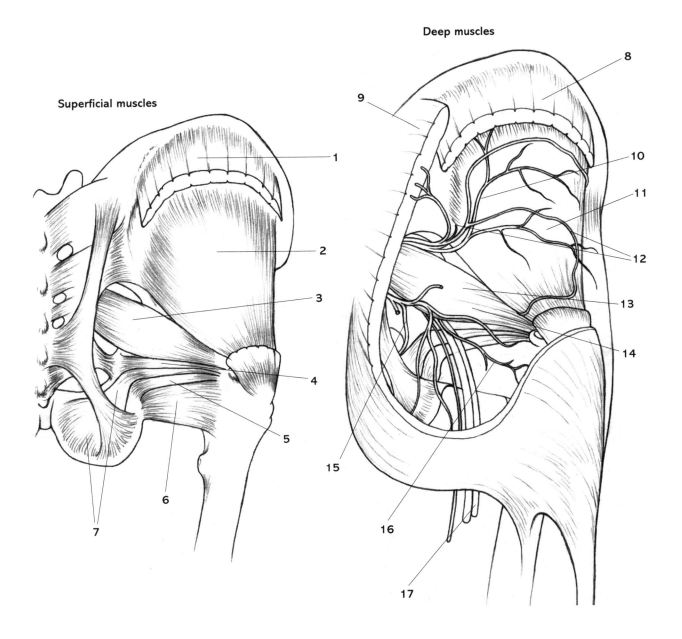

**Deep muscles**

**Superficial muscles**

Key: **1.** gluteus medius  **2.** gluteus minimus  **3.** piriformis  **4.** gemellus superior  **5.** gemellus inferior  **6.** quadratus femoris  **7.** obturator internus

**8.** gluteus medius  **9.** gluteus maximus  **10.** superior gluteal nerve  **11.** gluteus minimus  **12.** superior gluteal artery and vein  **13.** piriformis  **14.** inferior gluteal artery and vein  **15.** pudendal nerve  **16.** inferior gluteal nerve  **17.** sciatic nerve

## ANTERIOR AND POSTERIOR KNEE JOINT

The muscles that form the bulk of the anterior aspect of the thigh are primarily those of the quadriceps femoris. The four heads are the rectus femoris, the vastus lateralis, intermedius and medialis. They insert into the patella, which attaches to the tibial tubercle through the patellar ligament. The quadriceps femoris muscle is a powerful extensor of the knee joint. The other muscles on the anterior aspect of the thigh are the sartorius, going from the anterior superior iliac spine downwards and medially into the tibia, and, on the medial side, the gracilis, which is an adductor of the thigh.

## MEDIAL COMPARTMENT OF THE THIGH

The medial thigh muscles occupy what is known as the adductor, or medial compartment of the thigh. All these muscles are supplied by the obturator nerve. The adductor magnus has its uppermost part inserting into the upper aspect of the linear aspera or gluteal ridge. Other fibres run obliquely to the linear aspera, and the lowermost fibres run to the medial supracondylar ridge. The most distal fibres form the insertion into the adductor tubercle of the femur, with the distal fibres of the muscle forming the outline of the adductor hiatus, through which the femoral artery runs to become the popliteal artery.

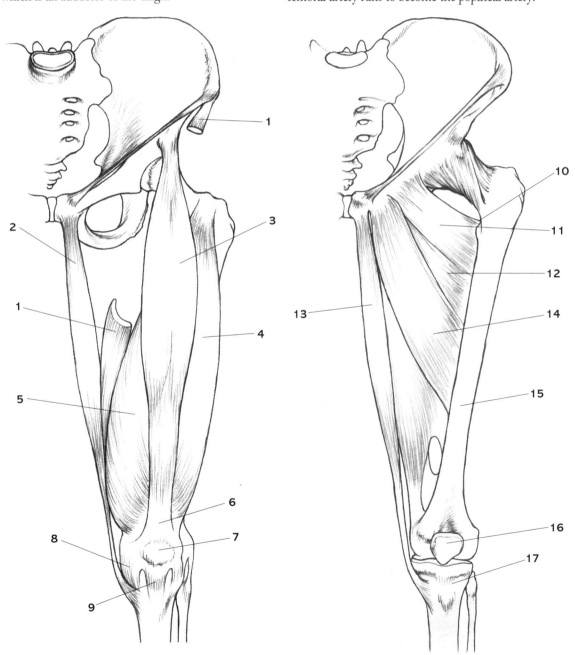

**Key**: **1.** sartorius  **2.** gracilis  **3.** rectus femoris  **4.** vastus lateralis  **5.** vastus medialis  **6.** quadriceps femoris tendon  **7.** patella  **8.** medial collateral ligament of the knee  **9.** patellar ligament

**10.** adductor magnus  **11.** pectineus  **12.** adductor brevis  **13.** gracilis  **14.** adductor longus  **15.** femur  **16.** patella  **17.** tibia

## OPEN KNEE JOINT

This shows the distal articulation of the knee, consisting of the proximal tibia, the menisci, synovial folds, the anterior and posterior cruciate ligaments, and the patellar ligament with infrapatellar fat and fold. The femur has been removed here to expose the upper surface of the tibia. The medial meniscus and lateral meniscus are seen to be crescentic in shape, with the anterior cruciate ligament originating at the anterior surface of the tibia, under the synovial fold. The popliteus tendon inserts into the lateral aspect of the knee joint in the area of the meniscus, where there is a popliteal hiatus. The patellar ligament inserts into the tibial tubercle of the tibia on its anterior aspect and underlying the patellar ligament is the infrapatellar fat pad.

## ANTERIOR ASPECT OF THE KNEE JOINT

Anterior to the knee joint are the muscles that extend the knee with the sesamoid patella. The rectus femoris, vastus lateralis and vastus medialis combine to form the quadriceps femoris tendon, which inserts into the patella and proceeds as the patellar ligament inserted into the tibial tubercle. On the lateral side, the ilio-tibial tract inserts into the tibia. Next to this is the lateral collateral ligament of the knee. On the medial side, the medial collateral ligament is seen deep to the insertions of the tendons of semitendinosus, gracilis and sartorius muscles, forming the pes anserinus on the medial aspect of the proximal tibia. The quadriceps muscles extend the knee joint.

## POSTERIOR ASPECT OF THE KNEE JOINT

The illustration shows the knee joint from the posterior with the muscles removed. The posterior aspect of the femur with the condylar surfaces and the intracondylar notch are visible, together with the posterior aspect of the tibia and proximal fibula. The medial collateral ligament and the lateral collateral ligament are visible, while posterior to the knee joint the capsule is thickened by the oblique popliteal ligament more proximally. Also visible is the popliteus muscle, which runs from the tibia inserting into the lateral aspect of the knee joint and lateral meniscus. The popliteal muscle assists in stabilising the knee during flexion and has a rotational effect on the tibia with the knee in flexion.

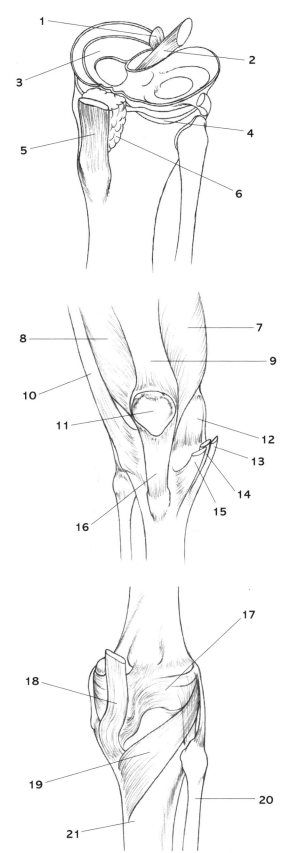

**Key: 1.** posterior cruciate ligaments  **2.** anterior cruciate ligaments  **3.** medial meniscus  **4.** lateral meniscus  **5.** patellar ligament  **6.** infrapatellar fat

**7.** vastus medialis  **8.** vastus lateralis  **9.** quadriceps femoris tendon  **10.** lateral collateral ligament and ilio-tibial tract  **11.** patella  **12.** medial collateral ligament  **13.** tendons of semitendinosus  **14.** gracilis  **15.** sartorius  **16.** patellar ligament

**17.** oblique popliteal ligament  **18.** semitendinosus tendon  **19.** popliteus muscle  **20.** fibula  **21.** tibia

## POPLITEAL FOSSA

The popliteal fossa is the space behind the knee joint and is a diamond-shaped space. The borders of the space are the semitendinosus and semimembranosus muscles on the medial side proximally and the biceps femoris muscle on the lateral side proximally. Distally the medial and lateral heads of gastrocnemius form the distal boundaries. The floor of the fossa is formed by the posterior aspect of the femur and tibia with part of the popliteus muscle, and the posterior capsule of the hip joint. Structures running within the popliteal fossa include the popliteal artery and vein. The artery lies close to the bone, with the vein more superficial. The sciatic nerve has inevitably divided into the tibial and fibular nerve prior to its arrival into the popliteal fossa. The common fibular nerve is seen to run on the lateral margin of the proximal part of the popliteal fossa, while the tibial nerve passes through the centre of it, running distally. Pathological swellings that may occur within the popliteal fossa include Baker's cyst and popliteal artery aneurysm.

**Popliteal fossa**

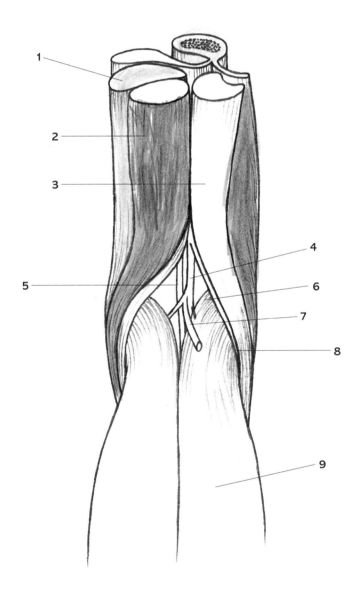

**Key: 1.** semimembranosus  **2.** semitendinosus  **3.** biceps femoris  **4.** tibial nerve  **5.** popliteal artery  **6.** plantaris **7.** popliteal vein  **8.** common fibular nerve  **9.** heads of gastrocnemius

## POSTERIOR COMPARTMENT OF THE LEG

The posterior compartment of the leg between the knee and the ankle contains large muscles, including the gastrocnemius, the soleus and the smaller plantaris muscle. The two heads of the gastrocnemius form the bulk of the proximal calf muscles and join together to form part of the Achilles tendon. Deep to this is the soleus muscle, and between the two is the plantaris muscle. The small plantaris with the long tendon suggests a little used vestigial muscle.

## LATERAL COMPARTMENT OF THE LEG

This is a lateral view of the posterior compartment muscles of the leg. The illustration shows the posterior muscles of the calf from the lateral viewpoint. The deep relationship of the soleus to the gastrocnemius is well seen. It is clear from the drawing that this muscle lies posterior to the axis of the flexion axis of the knee joint, and therefore flexes the knee, and posterior to the plantar flexion axis of the ankle joint, thereby acting as a powerful plantar flexor or flexor of the ankle joint.

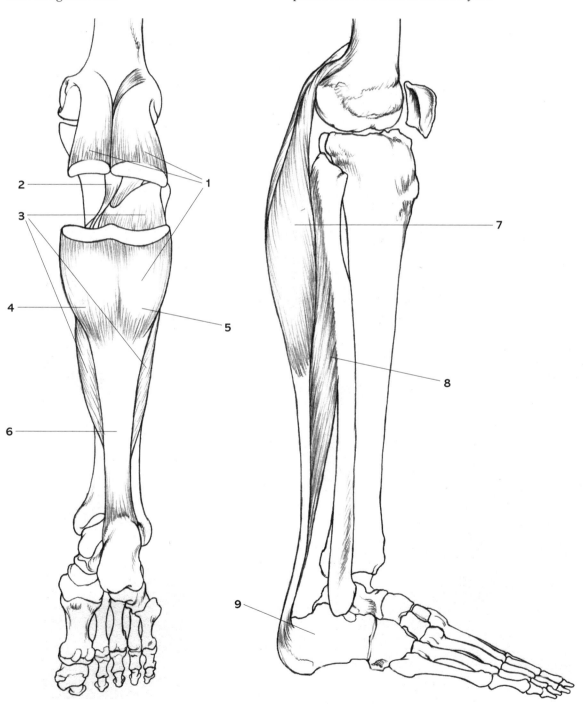

**Key: 1.** gastrocnemius  **2.** plantaris  **3.** soleus  **4.** medial head of gastrocnemius  **5.** lateral head of gastrocnemius
**6.** Achilles tendon

**7.** gastrocnemius  **8.** soleus  **9.** calcaneus

## LATERAL COMPARTMENT OF THE LEG

This lateral view of the right leg shows the tibia and fibula, ankle joint, subtalar joint and joints of the foot. Proximally, the fibular nerve is seen to wind around the neck of the fibula. Behind the lateral malleolus of the fibula are the tendons of the fibularis brevis and longus. The fibularis brevis is deep and closer to the bone. Both muscles plantarflex the ankle and evert it. The fibularis longus and brevis are supplied by the superficial fibular or musculocutaneous nerve, cutaneous branches of which go to the dorsum of the foot. The nerve passes between the fibularis muscles and the long extensors of the toes.

## ANTERIOR COMPARTMENT OF THE LEG

The muscles in the anterior compartment of the leg are lateral to the anterior margin of the tibia, which forms the subcutaneous surface. The four muscles in this group cross the ankle anterior to its axis of dorsiflexion and therefore dorsiflex (extend) the ankle. The extensor hallucis longus extends the big toe, with extension of all joints from the ankle distally towards the big toe. The extensor digitorum longus divides into four tendons, each going to the distal phalanx of the lesser toes and extending them. They also extend the ankle and provide some extension movement of the midtarsal joints and metatarsophalangeal joints. The fibularis tertius has an extensor effect on the ankle and hind foot joints.

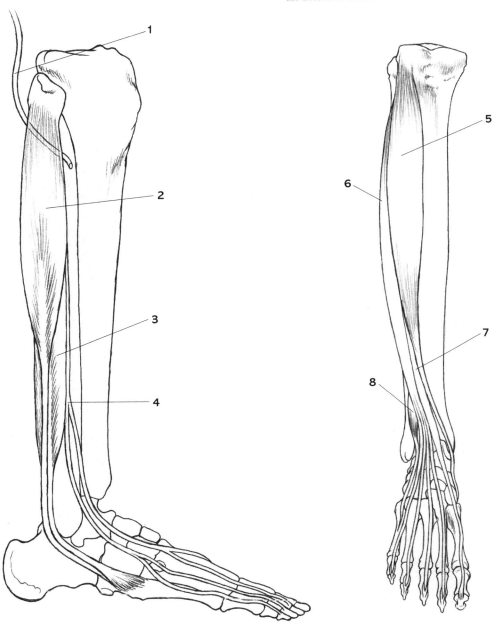

Key: 1. deep fibular nerve  2. fibularis longus  3. fibularis brevis  4. superficial fibular nerve

5. tibialis anterior  6. extensor digitorum longus  7. extensor hallucis longus  8. fibularis tertius

## MEDIAL LIGAMENTS OF THE ANKLE JOINT

This joint lies between the tibia and the fibula proximally and the talus distally. Its movements are almost all flexion and extension or plantar flexion and dorsiflexion. On the medial side of the ankle an anterior tibio-talar ligament combines with the tibio-navicular and tibio-calcaneal ligaments to form the medial ligament complex. A plantar calcaneonavicular ligament runs inferiorly to stabilise the medial side of the hind-foot as it merges with the mid-foot. Dorsal ligaments between the talus and the navicular as well as between the navicular and the tarsus provide further stability. The posterior aspect of the ankle joint is stabilised by the posterior tibio-fibular ligament, which prevents diastasis between tibia and fibula.

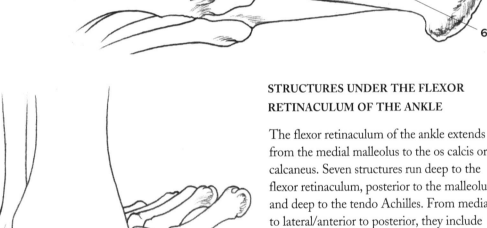

## STRUCTURES UNDER THE FLEXOR RETINACULUM OF THE ANKLE

The flexor retinaculum of the ankle extends from the medial malleolus to the os calcis or calcaneus. Seven structures run deep to the flexor retinaculum, posterior to the malleolus and deep to the tendo Achilles. From medial to lateral/anterior to posterior, they include the tibialis posterior tendon, flexor digitorum longus tendon, posterior tibial artery and vein, and the posterior tibial nerve. Inferior to these is the flexor pollicis longus tendon. These structures all course posterior and lateral to the ankle to reach the plantar surface of the foot. The tendons plantar-flex the ankle or the toes, depending on whether they go to the digits, the hallux or the bones of the mid-foot. They also invert the subtalar joint because of their position in relation to the movement of that joint. The posterior tibial artery is palpable as a pulse behind the medial malleolus and is often used to assess circulation to the foot.

**Key: 1.** tibiotalar ligament  **2.** tibionavicular  **3.** tibiocalcaneal ligament  **4.** sustentaculum tali of os calcis
**5.** tubercle of navicular bone  **6.** plantar calcaneonavicular ligament

**7.** tibialis posterior  **8.** flexor digitorum longus  **9.** posterior tibial artery  **10.** posterior tibial vein  **11.** posterior tibial nerve  **12.** flexor hallucis longus tendon

## EXTENSOR RETINACULUM AT THE ANKLE

The extensor retinaculum is composed of fibrous bands running from medial to lateral on the dorsal aspect. These bands prevent bow-stringing of the tendons and neurovascular structures and increase the mechanical advantage of the tendons as they dorsiflex or extend the ankle and the toes. The main extensor retinaculum runs from tibia to fibula, while the inferior extensor retinaculum runs from lateral to medial, dividing into superior and inferior parts. Deep to the main extensor retinaculum run the tibialis anterior tendon, the anterior tibial artery, the extensor hallucis longus tendon and the extensor digitorum. Deep to the inferior extensor retinaculum are the extensor digitorum longus tendons, the tendon of extensor hallucis longus and the tibialis anterior. On the more distal medial limb of the inferior extensor retinaculum run the extensor hallucis longus and the dorsalis pedis artery. The tendon of the extensor hallucis longus inserts into the extensor surface of the distal phalanx of the hallux, while the tendons of extensor digitorum longus insert into the distal phalanges of the other four toes. The fibularis tertius is a separate muscle that forms the lateral-most part of the extensor digitorum longus going to the base of the fifth metatarsal.

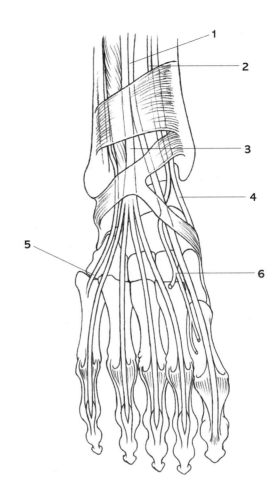

## ANKLE FIBULAR RETINACULUM

Looking at the lateral aspect of the ankle, the fibularis longus and brevis run posterior to the lateral malleolus, under the superior and inferior fibular retinacula, to insert into the cuboid (fibularis longus) and base of the fifth metatarsal (fibularis brevis). The fibularis brevis is closer to the fibula proximal to the ankle. Because of their position and direction in relation to the axis of movement, both tendons plantar-flex the ankle and evert it. Both muscles are supplied by the superficial branch of the common fibular nerve.

**Key: 1.** extensor hallucis longus  **2.** anterior tibial artery  **3.** extensor digitorum longus  **4.** tibialis anterior
**5.** fibularis tertius  **6.** dorsalis pedis artery

**7.** fibularis brevis tendons  **8.** fibularis longus  **9.** superior fibular retinaculum  **10.** inferior fibular retinaculum

# INDEX